Dear James

~ Letters *from a* Wren *in* World War II ~

Susan Slater

Illustrated by Helen Ridehalgh

~ Published by ~
BARNY BOOKS • Hough-on-the-Hill • Grantham • Lincs.

~ Produced by ~
TUCANN *design&print* • 19 High Street • Heighington • Lincoln LN4 1RG.
Telephone & Fax: (01522) 790009

ACKNOWLEDGEMENTS

My heartfelt thanks go to two friends, without whom this book would never have seen daylight; Brenda Bagshaw *(ex-WRAC)*, for her professional secretarial help and Helen Ridehalgh, for her delightful illustrations.

Also, for permission to use photographs, my thanks go to Mrs Ray Freeman of Dartmouth History Research Group, Ralph and Frances Cawthorne of Dartmouth Museum, Wren Gladys Studd *(McLaughlin)* and L/Wren Barbara Kneebone *(Lorentzen)*.

PREFACE

~ by Helen Ridehalgh ~

ANNA

JAMES and many service friends were frequent visitors at the 16th Century farmhouse of Anna's family. Two RAF and two Army Camps were swallowing up acres of farmland within 20 miles of her house. Social life enjoyed a peak period for a very limited spell. One of Anna's sisters went for her Naval VAD training and sailed to Australia; another sister was in the WRAF as a Plotting Officer; and a younger brother was in tanks in Africa, leaving two brothers to help on the farm. Anna, who volunteered for the WRNS, was called up to be a Wren Steward in May 1940, but she calmly wrote to WRNS Headquarters that there was promise of a bumper corn harvest that year and she felt she would be better helping with that, and could she be a Wren in the autumn. Contrary to the shocked reaction of family and friends, the Royal Navy *(bless them!)* saw sense in this and said she could join in September as a Supply Rating.

In Autumn 1940 Anna went off to Greenwich to train as a Wren.

JAMES

JAMES, a fighter pilot, was shot down in the Battle of Britain, horribly burned and wounded. He spent many months in a Military Hospital not too far from his father's estate in Scotland. There followed months of skin grafts and other treatment in and out of hospital. Except for his parents he didn't want to see anyone. Gradually he was sufficiently strong to ride his Mothers' old hunter and do some rough rounds on the estate. Later he and the Factor's son invented a small solid tractor-like vehicle - *"The Pram"* - which could tackle the more accessible terrain. Together with two faithful dogs, acres of land were handed over into his care.

Inevitably, the constant strain and effort took their toll and James died as Anna was returning to Civilian life.

Dear James

The long, golden, glorious and exhausting harvest came to an end. As planned, I left on Saturday for this totally different world.

To begin with - an alien London. Gone forever the old familiar rush of anticipation as one's train drew slowly - all too slowly - towards the meeting on the platform - the instant mad dash towards Underground or bus; hell bent for the last day of Harrods Sale or a Theatre or the end-of-Christmas-Term First Orchestra Concert at the R.C.M.

Arriving here now, I was suddenly jolted into the real wartime London - windows boarded; little heaps of rubble pushed away into odd corners, a greyish pallor of dust over all, but chiefly, I think it was the waiting figures as I emerged from the Underground station. Early afternoon, yet they were gathering to be first in the queue the moment they should be allowed down to find a sleeping place on a platform. Old, frail men and women; mothers with patient faces, their children clustering about them; silent, unprotesting. Each and every one clasping the bundle of blankets, the packs of food, the thermos flasks. Bringing up the rear, a one-armed man playing a small squeaky gramophone.

In Greenwich, each evening, the long caravans of lorries laden with refugees from their own homes, are the Eastenders escaping into the Kentish countryside to seek peace and sleep and shelter under the hedgerows, anywhere away from the bombing.

The terrible dockland fires have petered out but the air is still thick with lingering smoke. It attacks the tongue with an acrid taste.

Here inside the gates of R.N College (Greenwich Palace, in truth) we Pro-Wrens are allocated to Queen Anne Wing and have glorious lofty staterooms for our cabins and bed covers of snowy white with anchors woven into the centre. Alas, I do not think we shall ever sleep there, for each evening we collect our bedclothes and take them down into the vaults which are our air-raid shelters. I had never envisaged sleeping every night for weeks on end in a wine cellar, one of a succession of stone-arched vaults opening off a long underground passage. The flagged floors are covered with coconut matting and each vault holds about six mattresses. These are leaned up on end along the walls to air during the daytime but our bedding we carry back to those pristine beds, to await the reverse procedure at dusk.

It is quite blissfully safe down below and in addition, we have a Destroyer moored on the river, just under our walls. Her sole duty: to protect the College.

Every time she fires her guns, we shout our thanks and bellow encouragement; sounding for all the world like a mob of third-formers at a school hockey match. But it would seem the only way of expressing our gratitude.

Daylight raids are frustrating and time-consuming as we must go to the underground shelters and there remain until the 'All Clear'.

I long to explore this Queen Anne Wing but there is never the time to do that. I would not go alone as I have little sense of direction and one could get so completely lost. There is an overwhelming sense of history within these walls; the past so very close to the edges of the present; you can almost hear it rustling, whispering. Reach out and you will touch something. To round a corner and come upon King Hal himself or one of his hapless Queens would prompt an instant deep curtsey and little surprise. Scarcely a raised eyebrow. However, no time for all that.

Recruiting has moved elsewhere because of the bombing. So, no intake of personnel but drafting out continues and our department is becoming markedly short-handed. Speaking mathematically, each Wren is doing the work of two and seven-eighths Wrens. No one minds; no one complains; but by comparison, that harvest time was just a rural frolic.

Some nights, when at last I am stretched out in my wine cellar, I lie with tears - floods of quite involuntary tears - coursing down my cheeks. And I had always believed that 'tears of exhaustion' were something invented by the more flowery novelists! I am not in the least unhappy and I would not be anywhere else that I can think of.

The mattress on my right is now occupied by a bookworm, Penelope. Her books are her most treasured possessions and she brings them down to safety each night. She reads to me; poetry mostly - Houseman, Yeats, Spender. Sometimes bits of Jane Austen. I look forward to these brief sessions.

We are getting fogs from the river. Strange how they creep through the vast iron gates and invade the courtyard. So thick the atmosphere some mornings, you feel you could reach out and push it apart. Well, it is almost November and at least the fog gives us some short respite from the raids.

I must now confirm that I am a fully-fledged Wren, the probationary period being over and ending a terrible and completely sleepless night which I could not, and indeed never shall understand.

Never mind, I was issued with my uniform. Skirt reaching almost to the ground and shoes crippling beyond the point of torture. We were given a half-day's leave after enrolment; so, feeling I must air the fact that I am really in the Royal Navy, I twisted up surplus skirt around my waist, fixed my tallyband (HMS PEMBROKE) onto the hat and went off to catch a river steamer to Woolwich. (Marine transport seemed to be called for, even if it was only a Thames river steamer.) I was the sole passenger waiting on the jetty at Greenwich and the siren started wailing. Presently, the buzz of a plane and guns began to fire.

There was not a vestige of shelter on that small jetty. Anyhow, 'Stand your ground' I told myself. 'It sounds like just an odd one and there's plenty of protective gunfire, it won't get through.' And I was right. The All Clear sounded. A few more passengers congregated as the steamer rounded the bend. Nevertheless, there had been time to wonder whether, if the worst happened, could a newly-enrolled Wren be eligible for a funeral with full Naval honours? I doubted it.

We were still overworked and undermanned when my Draft came through. I appealed against it on the grounds that, because of acute personnel shortages, I was less than halfway through my training. But without success. I had one last go, requesting to see the Commanding Officer. 'I am sorry to worry you Ma'am', I began, and said my piece.

'Tyler,' she said, 'you are not worrying me. Not in the least.' She smiled pleasantly, 'If you call in at the Regulating Office, Chief Wren will give you your railway warrant. You report to HMS Nemo tomorrow.' She proffered a hand. I took it, stepped back to attention, wheeled and walked smartly from the room and in the direction of the Regulating Office to discover just whereabouts HMS Nemo might be.

So it was to be my last night in the vaults. I did not relish in the least that unknown fate into which I should be forced to launch myself on the morrow. I hated the thought of leaving Penelope and our nightly readings. And the safety of our surroundings, protected by the Destroyer without, and the Marine sergeants within. Two distant shadowy figures standing guard where the dark passages branched off to goodness knows where. And nearer and not at all shadowy, the handsome Sergeant Peters. The vault next to ours has been transformed into a Sick Bay with an R.N Nursing Sister and a VAD on nightly duty. From their alcove, the shaded light casts a pale primrose patch onto the opposite wall. There is something positive about this if one wakes, confused, during the night. And something homely and reassuring in the gentle hiss of their kettle as Sister prepares tea for the two of them and the Sergeant. Each night prior to lights out, we have Sick Bay routine, headed by Sister, administering the odd cough lozenge to this one and that at her discretion. VAD follows, bearing a tiny tray with medicine glasses. Bringing up the rear, Sergeant Peters, armed with a powerful torch. This he shines along the floor, pausing here and there to drop on one knee, smooth the blankets and gently tuck them in. To have one's feet tucked in by a Sergeant of Marines - well, what more could one ask of life?

Come the daylight, of course, it is a very different matter. The Sergeant, having distanced himself into the real Serviceman's world, is busy picking up shrapnel, fallen overnight into our courtyard. Impeccably turned out, not noticing anyone, filling up the red bucket with a wealth of lethal bits - "The Cruel Confetti" someone has called it.

A couple of hours later will find us standing before him on the parade ground and likely as not experiencing the sharp end of his tongue. No cosiness out there. We shall all be in our rightful places.

The woods at home will be deep in fallen leaves now. I think of them, quiet and settled for the long night of another winter.

Tell me what goes on in the farming world.

Anna

Dear James

It was on an afternoon of thick fog and matching mood of gloom that I took my leave of Greenwich and my friends there and made my way to the point of departure from London.

The journey from thence was so strange as to be almost unreal. A short wait on a bomb-scarred railway station; the platform a deserted stage, its battered props leaning at precarious angles; the players long since driven away by disaster from without. Over all, a feeling that the everyday dramas peculiar to other railway stations had no part here. No joyous re-unions, tearful partings, brisk precision-timed business appointments or cheerful, rackety day trips to Clacton on a bright summer's morning. These belonged to happier places.

I studied the ancient locomotive. It looked barely strong enough to remain upright on its wheels and I noted that no mechanic came alongside, tapping those wheels with some checking instrument.

It was a non-corridor train and my compartment cold, clammy and unkempt. I heard no whistle as we started. There is a war on; we must economize on man-power. Or maybe we looked too down-trodden to merit a send-off.

The engine clanked, retched into motion and we swayed and jolted away from a sort of civilization and into the fog.

It was mid-afternoon but already daylight was turning its back on us. Outside my window and well below the railway embankment, mud flats merging into the general murkiness. And just discernible, stout mooring posts in lonely isolation; waiting till the incoming tide should make its furtive advances and creep about them with scarcely a sound.

The line, safely elevated above this impenetrable waste, could run on to the edge of the world and beyond. I began to feel apprehensive, now recollecting that I had not actually seen any other passengers boarding this train. I had busied myself getting the two suitcases and gas mask into the compartment.

Was I the sole passenger and - worse - was I in the wrong train? Was there even an engine driver? Or could this worn out locomotive be destined for demolition, and the victim of some wartime economy scheme whereby the stoker fuelled her up, driver released the brakes, they both jumped back onto the platform, mopped their faces, took off their hats as a token of respect, relief and farewell and that was it?

The little remaining daylight seemed to have left us - that is, the train and me. For by now I was almost convinced that there was no one else and I was alone on this final journey. It seemed an ignominious sort of end, just to be spirited out of the world into a grey eternal mist and no one to see even the flutter of my handkerchief waving goodbye. We went on and on. I was now sitting on the edge of the seat, straining my eyes into the gloom. Then, something was different; our pace slowing and bulky shapes appearing quite close beside us. Buildings. A convulsive jerk and several minor shudders. We had stopped and were in the real world. I lost not a moment in getting luggage and self onto the platform and back into reality. None too easy in the strangeness and the strict blackout. There were shadowy figures by the exit. One, in familiar uniform, came towards me.

'Wren Tyler?' 'Yes.' Then, 'I am Bowen. I have come to take you to your billet.' She seized one case and switched on her torch. I was being piloted into the unknown.

And what that may hold, well, you shall hear in due course.

Anna

Dear James

For several days the fog has persisted. It is not the soft grey veiling mist of early Autumn mornings. Too late in the year for that. We are into winter now and this dripping, dense gloom shuts out everything that lies beyond my daily route from billet to Base. From the red brick villa, then round a corner and down a long, long street of small houses with front gardens bordering the pavement.

At the end of this, the Naval Base. The main building, a three storey hotel by the jetty. For the rest, an assortment of offices, stores and sheds; formerly the premises of the local Yacht Club.

At the eastern edge, a high wire fence with heavily-guarded gateway, surrounds the shipyard. Here the workers stream in each morning, showing their passes and carrying gas-masks and luncheon packs. Here, day long the machinery drones, giant saws scream their way through timbers, men shout and over all, shrill bells alarm, alert and punctuate the working day.

This then, is our background, for our place of work in a small flat above a boat house, lies immediately outside the guarded entrance. And our particular office, the galley at the head of an open stairway. The galley work top, running its very limited length, provides the communal desk for Chief, in a chair by the window; then on three high stools, myself sandwiched between the two Petty Officers. Elbow room certainly takes on a new meaning.

I had not seen Wren Bowen since she met me at the railway station on the night of my arrival. We had stopped briefly, on the way to my billet to report to the Wren Officer. At the billet we had parted, Bowen saying, 'Well, good luck and you are going to need it working for that Chief!' My sinking spirits were in no way uplifted by Deirdre, who shares the billet. Her comment was: 'Terrible old man, that Chief. Everyone knows about him. He puts the fear of death into one and all.'

Deirdre, an ash blonde with broad Suffolk accent, wide, cornflower blue eyes and a throaty chuckle, is a sort of miniature Mae West. The soul of good nature, popular with the landlady's children and every sailor's dream girl. Their cries of 'Hi Blondie!' and 'Mornin' Snowball!' delight her as she hurries along the waterfront at 0800 hours each morning. As our hours of duty are never the same and her social life takes care of her evenings, Deirdre and I see little of one another.

Our Wren Officer, I have not seen since the brief reporting call on my arrival. More than a little eccentric I had thought her - well, a strange bird, certainly. Something definitely bird-like in the way she flapped her long arms and slapped her knee to emphasize a point; at the same time, throwing back her head to reveal very large, even teeth, and emitting a loud noise, an alarming combination of caw and cackle. And I stood there before her, wondering what on earth could be the joke. Perhaps it was due to the fog and the journey and my overpowering fatigue that it escaped me.

As for Chief, returned from retirement to serve for the duration of this war; here is a tall, angular Welshman with a slight stoop, jerky movements (something vaguely un-co-ordinated somewhere), strong Welsh accent, long, thin nose, ever-so-slightly out of line; pale, pale blue eyes. On the rare occasions when he has been obliged to address me directly, a loud sniff and the word 'Miss', have both heralded and concluded those few words, obviously wrung from him by dire necessity.

For my part 'I keep my head down' as they say and never, ever volunteer a remark.

The two Petty Officers, on Shore duty after active service, both are survivors (one from the Ark Royal so I am told). They do not ever talk about it. They have cottages in the village here and their wives, one expecting her first child, have joined them. I feel thankful and happy for them. Both are wonderfully helpful, steering me along, since the work here is one deep, uncharted sea. Seriously I wonder if I shall survive. But I receive silent help from left and right. A scribbled instruction here, a muttered correction of word or figure under the breath, are lifebelts thrown out to me in my constant flounderings. I am ever grateful and if I do survive, it will be due entirely to these two young men.

Now, at last the fog has lifted and I am able to form some idea of my wider surroundings. The built-up area of small houses and shops thins out to landward and ends in a large expanse of grassy common-land; too irregular perhaps for a village green but with sizeable, attractive houses spaced about its perimeter. The Church stands at the farthest end. Farmlands and marshlands stretch inwards from the sea in an eternity of flatness. One is ever conscious of the sky in this sort of landscape. So much of it and nothing to break it up until

it merges with the earth on that far, far horizon. Something remote and mysterious in that meeting of sky and fens. You find yourself stretching your eyes but the distance defeats them; you screw them up, thinking that might bring eve-

rything nearer. You have not changed anything and still you do not know whether that faint, dark smudge could be a barn or a clump of trees or maybe a birdwatcher's hide-out. The marshes have their own secrets.

Time off from work, for me, consists of every Sunday afternoon and one Saturday half-day per fortnight. Sunday afternoons are devoted to hockey matches. Mixed hockey for Naval Officers and Wrens. It is years since I handled a hockey stick and this, my first introduction to mixed hockey, I find totally hazardous! One of the Officers, who in peace-time played for Europe, gives us half-an-hour's coaching before the game begins. This is a gruelling experience. And the game which follows - well! I just use my stick in self defence. Never mind who gets the ball or what they choose to do with it.

Last week there were shadowy figures in the distant pavilion. Turning to a callow young sub-lieutenant, I asked, 'Who are those people?'

When he had finally struggled out of his cable-knit sweater, he said, 'Oh those. They are the stretcher-bearers.' I did not know whether to be comforted or more terrified. I tossed my head.

'Actually, I now recollect that the WVS are borrowing extra tea-urns for their AGM tomorrow.' Well, he might be my superior on the hockey field but when it came to the field of imagination, he had met his equal.

After play is over, the Officers invite us back to tea in their Mess. With nothing more lethal than a cup of tea in the hand, really they appear quite human.

Anna

HMS NEMO
February 1941

Dear James

Christmas came and went. The monochrome of our daily routine only slightly and briefly coloured by a small gathering for sherry in Ships Office and another more crowded affair at the Officers' Club. It was friendly enough but rather quiet; everyone, I guess, immersed in their own thoughts. Many like myself, thankful they said, not to be on leave.

The WVS entertained us to a midday dinner at the Naval Club, thus giving our landladies and their families the day to themselves. We stayed on and danced through the evening.

End of January and my first leave.
Closing the door on the billet at 0600 and out into the starlight and a

bitter frost. The village still asleep, its inhabitants cocooned in indoor warmth.

Some muffled activity when I reached the Base. Being hoisted up into the back of a Naval truck and piloted to a generous space between two young sailors was the start of the journey. Not much conversation, no visibility; a rubbery smell of gas masks and the unmistakable aroma of illicit rum being passed around in the darkness. And thus I was jolted towards the first early morning train on the nearest main line.

It was almost midnight when the journey ended. A full moon and I knew the way. I supposed that was all that was needed. A three-and-a-half mile walk lay ahead. Down the station yard, over the river bridge, up through the deserted streets and quiet alleyways; over a second bridge to the rising stretch of

road. That the snow was too deep for any short cuts across the field paths was no surprise. I tackled the longer route with just the moon watching and the glistering whiteness surrounding me. Winter had the upper hand.

The Leave became a short period of activities related to walking. Riding being ruled out and cycling abandoned after a couple of perilous experiences.

The new vicar and his wife ski-ed over to tea one afternoon, enthusing over the perfect weather conditions for their current mode of travel. They have recently returned from some vast Canadian parish. I sent up a fervent, silent prayer that my Father would not appear at that moment, for neither he nor many of their farming parishioners here, were sharing such enthusiasm. Every available hand was set to the feeding and watering of the livestock, the breaking of ice on water troughs and the never-ending thawing of innumerable taps and pipes. So much in demand were the boiling kettles for this purpose, that the simple everyday making of a cup of tea suddenly became an exercise in low cunning. For, unless a continuous watch were kept, one, two, or even three kettles could disappear in a matter of seconds. There were not enough of them to go around and kettle snatching became rife in our household. For example...I find the wide back door fully open and the muffled figure of stockman, Boddy, blocking entrance or exit. 'All the kettles are out,' I say dismissively and move to close the door. But Boddy is not budging. With the intensity of a hungry stoat sighting a rabbit, his eyes are fixed on the distant kitchen range.

'What's in yon pan?' he demands, darkly.

'Dinner,' I fabricate, a shade more darkly, in the third desperate attempt to rescue our coffee break. And so it goes on...

Anna

HMS NEMO
March 1941

Dear James

Returning from leave to a pleasant surprise. A new office. Our department has moved to premises situated within the shipyard. Well, just inside the guarded gateway. A newly built single storey block, flat roofed and of red brick.

The office space, by comparison with that just vacated, seems positively palatial. A desk each, facing three walls. Chief on the west side, two Petty officers south and myself east; whilst the north wall houses a magnificent large black stove. This is efficiently tended by a young stoker and makes a world of difference to our working day throughout the bitter cold of the early months of this new year.

These winds have to be experienced to be believed. 'Blowing straight from Siberia,' say the natives here. Nowadays everyone rushes. No one walks. All are muffled figures shrunk within scarves, hoods, duffel coats, so as to be unrecognizable. Just bundles of clothing in a hurry; nobody pausing or stopping to talk. A hasty wave of the mittened hand or similar gesture of recognition, is all one friend can expect of another in conditions so arctic.

The new office entrance is beside my desk, thus giving me the advantage of seeing who may be coming or going. A second door exactly opposite this one is, for some reason, used only by Chief. I have a sneaking feeling that he keeps the key despite the ruling that during off-duty hours, all keys are to be surren-

11

dered to Master at Arms and never taken off the premises.

Three weeks later...

The weather shows some improvement at last, the wind now losing its bite and a weak, shy hovering sunshine gracing the odd day.

It was on one such day, a working Saturday, that as usual I stayed in the office whilst the men went to lunch. They had wives with their dinners ready. I had a landlady who did not seem to mind at what hour we came to meals. There was one cooking time and whoever came late found her portion keeping warm in the side oven. The cloth was always on the table and last meals merged into next.

This particular day, the shipyard machinery was silent, all shut down until Monday morning. No clamour, no voices. Now that we actually worked alongside the sheds, the noise seemed less penetrating, for it had become the established atmosphere. When it ceased, the silence, instead of becoming the blessed relief which one would have expected, had an uneasy quality.

Sorting out my next batch of work, I realised that something was interfering with that silence. I gave it my full attention. The faint buzzing was becoming less faint as the seconds passed. I now knew what it was. The sirens wailed. What to do? Not a lot of choice.

'Keep as low down as possible and protect your face,' was a piece of advice I had been given years ago. That had applied to a car accident and was

hardly relevant to this current situation. But it seemed sensible. I crept under my desk and covered my face with both hands. I felt rather lonely but nothing else in particular.

A bomb screeched down and exploded. Another followed and there was a tremendous bang and a clattering on our flat roof as if an army of giants were stampeding up there. Then, gunfire from the opposite bank of the river and the sound of a plane making a quick getaway. Then silence. It seemed to be over. With caution, I emerged, straightened myself out and studied the ceiling. It looked all right, no cracks visible. At that instant, Chief's door burst open and I was suddenly confronted by something... or someone...

For one lightning moment, I was standing on the cart track at home. There was a field of sprouting wheat and a newly-erected scarecrow...

Then blinking hard, I came to and Chief's breathing became more controlled, his hands dropped to his sides.

'You all right Miss?'

'Yes Chief, thank you. Yes, I am all right.'

I continued to stare at the hatless, tieless, collarless figure. Shirt sleeves flapping with cuffs unbuttoned. Black braces, no jacket.

But it was the carpet slippers which riveted my attention. Their green and red tapestry design - oh, so unmistakably Welsh. The dark, forbidding mountains, the green, green valleys; the coal pits; the male-voice choirs; the words containing all twenty-six letters of the alphabet. *All* were embroidered into those slippers.

In silence we continued to assess one another. And then behind Chief and through the open door, came the two Petty Officers. They had been running hard but both were correctly dressed.

The same question, 'You all right Miss?'

Their faces registered no surprise at what else they saw and they made no remark. Chief addressed me.

'Best go now Miss and you won't be expected back this side of morning. Would you like one of the P.O's to go with you?'

'Thank you, Chief, I can manage. Really, I am all right. I will be here in the morning.' I gathered up my gas-mask.

Halfway up the long street, I met the hurrying white-faced figure of Mrs M, (our landlady), her apron still on, her husband's coat thrown about her shoulders.

'I left the kiddies next door. I had to come. They said it was the shipyard - a direct hit and two dead. I didn't know what to expect.'

We reached home. 'Your dinner's dried up,' she apologised. 'I'll make you something.'

'Just a cup of tea for both of us,' I said.

I felt suddenly very tired.

Anna

13

Dear James

It was a quiet morning in the office. The two Petty Officers on duty elsewhere, Chief deep in a huge ledger, the stove sputtering gently. Myself, halfway down a seemingly endless column of figures and scarcely aware of someone knocking, entering and crossing the floor. A pause, a query from Chief. Then the reply with a few sentences of explanation.

Suddenly, I found myself gazing not at figures but into a glossy programme, my hard chair became soft red plush; the footlights were on, the curtain up. I sat galvanized, entranced by the sheer magic of that voice.

Above the sound of rustling papers, Chief's muttered comments; an occasional query and answer. Then Chief's voice, 'All present and correct,' finality in his tone.

'Oh no!' I prayed that even at this eleventh hour there might come to light some glaring discrepancy requiring lengthy detailed explanation. Or, knowing Chief, the possibility of a minute irregularity would trigger off an immediate post mortem. Alas, my luck was out.

'Well, so-long,' said Chief, adding whatever in Welsh means 'Good luck go with you.'

'Thank you and good-day to you Chief.'

The floodlights switched off. My programme melted into thin air. I looked towards the door to see him go. Tall, slim figure; slight wave in the dark, well-brushed hair; an undeniably handsome face with a small trim beard; deep violet blue eyes, quizzical, humorous, turned for the briefest moment in my direction as he opened the door and was gone.

'Chief - who was that Petty Officer?' I asked.

The reply came, 'Dicky Olivier, Miss.'

'Olivier?'

'Yes Miss. Brother to the actor fellow, I understand. Turning in his gear just now and off for his Commission.'

I accosted the first knowledgeable Wren.

'Oh, Dicky Olivier,' she said. 'No-one ever saw much of him. Spent all his shore leave in London. Left here for good today, or so I'm told.'

The tennis and cricket seasons are approaching and the recreation ground is now the scene of some preparatory activity. I was aware of this since our landlady's orchard borders upon one corner of this particular field.

One day in the office, I was asked if I played tennis. I replied that I did play and was looking forward to the start of the season. Alas! Too late did I discover that I had been addressing a thrice county champion!

Hastily, I sought another Wren who had confessed to having cold feet over the approaching tennis season. We conferred, wrung our hands and made miserable moan. Then we agreed that we must make the attempt to be *positive*. Miriam, for that is her name, being a watchkeeper, would be free to look around in the daytime. Consequently, three days later I found a note awaiting me at the office in Miriam's enormous scrawl. She had arranged for the use of a hard tennis court for the early hours of three mornings per week. It had the major advantage of being on a remote site and behind buildings and at 7am (seven *a.m.* mark you), any activity there would scarcely attract much attention. No need, she assured me, to wear dark glasses, cultivate a limp or a foreign accent

or dye one's hair. So far, so good. Thus we started and it was *disastrous!* Miriam could not get one ball in five over the net, whereas I could not keep one inside even the perimeter high wire surrounding the courts. I slashed and volleyed like someone demented. We lost balls into back gardens and dare not knock on doors to retrieve them at that unsocial hour. Alternative to the gardens was a sort of magnetic slag heap with nettles to add to our agony. After about two weeks of this, humour took over and following on a long, wild burst of hysteria one morn-

ing about the hour of sunrise, we settled down and began to play something resembling the game of tennis.

Anna

HMS NEMO
April-May 1941

Dear James

Since my last letter, a new star has arisen in our Wren firmament. An Irish girl, Theresa McCoy, Tess to her friends.

'Have you seen the new Wren?' The question was going round before I set eyes on her.

Due to some hold-up in supplies of uniform, the newest entries are still in civilian dress. And there is no doubt that this one is taking full advantage of such a situation.

All heads are turned in her direction as she swings through the village in a variety of eye-catching garments. Tall, slim, square shoulders, enormous green eyes with quizzical pencilled brows. A retroussé nose and lovely, laughing mouth. Dark brown silken hair, shoulder length, and with a wide streak of gold down one side. Definitely worth a second glance.

Without any previous warning, Deirdre and I discovered that McCoy was to share our billet. I wondered how this would work out since already there are two infants and four adults. However, Deirdre continues as before and is rarely seen and the newcomer is a watchkeeper with frequent night duties. In addition, she spends most of her free days with her sister, wife of an Army Officer based some ten miles away. There, it would appear, they are never short of transport and lead a high-powered social life. Dinners, dances, parties and horse-riding. Tess asks me to go riding and I am sorely tempted, but on a Wren's weekly pay of twelve shillings and sixpence, how could I? So I content myself playing audience to the doubtless wildly exaggerated tales of Tess' many conquests, recounted in true Irish brogue and wicked humour.

She will creep in on her way to bed after these adventures and sit hunched on a spare couch in the corner of my room. Thus mindful of the two sleeping infants across the landing, we stifle our mirth.

On some mornings, just as I finish breakfast, Tess will come in from night duty and bursting with news. I have no time to dally so she snatches a piece of toast, spreads it with marg and marmalade and does an about turn towards the Base with me. There is a wide track running behind the houses and parallel with the main street. We choose this and I listen to the latest adventure, through scrunching toast. This newly-discovered route is a pleasant lane, bordered on one side by back gardens and the other by a hedge and fields. We have adopted this as our habitual route in dry weather and that hedgerow promises honey-suckle and wild roses when their time comes.

One evening, on my return from duty, I found Tess hopping with impatience. 'Hurry,' she said. 'Get into your best. We are going dancing.'

Cautiously, I said 'With whom and where?'

'Colchester, and with two Officers I've just met. They came in to send a signal. They are having some emergency with engines and have put in for repairs. Don't *please* look so sceptical. They're awfully presentable. I *promise* you'll approve and they have got tickets.'

'Not so fast,' I said. 'What about our Passes?'

'There was no time, and anyhow the Office was closed...I think...anyhow, it's too late now.'

'But I don't like it,' I said. 'We could be in trouble, especially with this

new Wren Officer.'

'Don't spoil it, don't spoil it,' she wailed.

'All right,' I said. 'But I still don't much like it.'

We hurried ourselves ready and the doorbell rang. The blackout successfully blacked out any hope of seeing clearly the two figures waiting to escort us to the gate where our taxi awaited us; an enormous, shuddering shape, surely a vintage model. Probably seen in the funeral procession of Queen Victoria; brass-rimmed lamps gleaming and, for that occasion, the windows veiled with mourning crêpe. It wheezed, the driver wheezed as he held open the wide door, his bulky figure muffled, shapeless in the dim light. The inside of this unusual vehicle was vast and smelling mightily of mothballs and general mustiness.

We started jerkily. The enforced turn, since we are at the end of the cul-de-sac, was made with some difficulty and the journey got under way. I had the feeling that our driver had not ventured further than the local railway station since the blackout came into force. Once clear of the houses, we pursued an uncertain, lurching course. Pale moonlight was shrouded by ground mist rising on either side.

There was only spasmodic conversation amongst the four passengers. Question and answer. A few involuntary gasps as we grazed the bank opposite and took a sudden swing to our own side. This seemed scarcely necessary since we had the road to ourselves all the way.

We must have been the last to arrive at the one large hotel in the town. Tess and I made our way to the cloakroom and what confronted us there left us gasping and reeling back against the wall. For on a long, broad shelf, backed by mirrors, were carefully placed at least one hundred Wren Officers' hats. The mirrors didn't help. They only doubled the number.

Weak and shaking, we looked at one another. The unspoken question: could SHE be here?

'There's one way to find out,' Tess said, sweeping two wide gangways between the hats, thus making three lots. She then produced an *enormous* tip

17

from her handbag and thrust it at the startled attendant. 'Now, you read all the names in that bunch,' she said, 'and if you come across this one,' printing it in large capitals on a paper towel, 'You just shout!' We went to work, quickly turning over each tricorne in our lot and examining the name tape.

Our luck seemed to be in. We made our way towards the sound of music and our waiting escorts.

One, Charles, was tall, fair and good looking with a rather dreamy expression in his grey eyes. The other, Shaun, shorter, stocky build; dark hair, twinkling blue eyes and sometimes an Irishness of speech rather than an accent.

The Royal Marine Band was superb and the food excellent. We began to enjoy ourselves. Everyone was R.N from an Admiral down to a Wren Cadet Officer with her white armband. And, of course, we two guilty Wrens, one in civilian clothes and attracting no adverse attention, the other completely vulnerable but hoping to pass unnoticed in the crowd.

Of our partners, I gleaned that Charles had just graduated from Cambridge with some sort of Marine Science degree. He thought that the Navy would at least keep him in touch with the sea. Shaun, sailing was his hobby, came from Dublin, was a member of The Abbey Theatre Company and a fascinating conversationalist.

It ended all too soon. Our driver, breathing liquor, and in full wheeze, shepherded us into the taxi.

Thus we started home with hope but little confidence. Once clear of the houses, it seemed less foggy. Glancing through the window, I became convinced that we had left the main road. The hedgerows seemed thicker and closer and more typical of the deep country. But we were moving, albeit a mite uncertainly.

We talked freely now. Shaun insisted that we sang. So we sang. Then began the real entertainment, our actor sitting on one of the tip-up seats with his back to the driver; we, the audience, on the broad seat facing him. What a night! 'Juno and the Paycock', then 'Pygmalion', lots more of Shaw. Then Shakespeare, sonnets, speeches, short extracts taking several parts from a scene. Then we would have a song or a Round. Then poetry, Yeats, Spender, Houseman, Hillaire Belloc. There were no lights, no pictures. It was a wireless Theatre. That voice, in turn commanding, wheedling, mocking, cursing, caressing.

All the emotions were there. The voice painted the pictures.

Thus we lurched our way back, arriving miraculously in one piece and were disgorged from our moving playhouse in the early hours.

'See you tonight,' was the parting chorus.

Early evening came, bringing Tess back from her afternoon Watch; tragedy written on her face.

'Anna, you wouldn't believe this.' She flopped down on a chair. 'Those beastly engineers have worked all night. They've broken some record. Our Boy-ohs have gone with the morning tide. They left this note!'

She handed the slip of paper to me. I read, 'Thanks for last night and sadly, farewell.'

'Anna, I want to cry. Let's cry together.'

'What did he quote last night?' I asked her.

'Something about the best goodbyes being said whilst the rose scarce i' the bud.'

Somewhat morosely...

Anna

HMS NEMO
May-June 1941

Dear James

The tennis season started. Miriam and I conferred and decided to study form from the sheltered distance of my landlady's orchard.

We waited. The collected white-clad figures spun rackets, paired off and play commenced. Presently, deep in conversation, apparently unobservant of anything or anyone in particular, we strolled to the farthest court, set slightly apart from the rest. Fortunate, we thought, this particular one was available. Our fortune was short-lived. Lost balls buried themselves deep in a wide ditch, an all too handy receptacle for the groundsman's cuttings and the breeding ground of a particularly vicious species of mosquito.

The red pin-pricks appearing on arms and legs, were transformed overnight into huge, white scorching blisters. But with next morning, the worst was yet to come. By the time I had forced black woollen stockings over feet and legs and encased my arms within the sleeves of a fitting navy serge jacket, I was on the verge of martyrdom and close to total collapse. Unable to face food, I sipped a little tea and staggered down the back lane, and shall never, ever know how I managed to get through that day.

A free weekend, total cessation of any activity and the application of *pints*

19

of calamine lotion, got me fit for duty by Monday morning.

Summer is really here with an endless succession of mornings misty with promise of a scorching day to follow. Wild roses and honeysuckle have taken over the hedgerow down our back lane. I felt homesick for hay time. Miriam said she had discovered acres of hay fields just beyond her billet. We planned an early morning sortie and crept out at 6am making for the dew-drenched fields to meet the sun.

We leaned over a gate at the edge of a field half-cut; flowers mingling with newly fallen grasses in the long swathes. Grass still living green. Marguerites, clovers, milkmaids and ladies fingers holding their bright colours for the last time.

All this brought back my earliest recollections of hay time. I suppose I was close on five and had insisted on carrying my Father's breakfast to the near meadow where, at 4am he had started cutting the grass. Betsy, entrusting the enamel can into my hand and saying 'Careful now lovey, and hold it well away from you,' and crooking my other arm through the handle of a small basket with a blue-check cloth covering the sandwiches of freshly fried bacon inside home-baked bread.

I remember vividly the dog daisies, as we called them and the wealth of clover in the grass; tall foxgloves on the bank and a wild rose bush beside the open gate. Standing well back as the horses, steady old Captain and a newly broken chestnut, came up the long field. I was surprised to see the young one and asked 'Why?'

'Better to use him at this time of day before the flies get bothersome,' I was told. 'And he's not steady enough yet for the men to handle him.'

There was a halt for breakfast. I knew better than to try feeding a handful of grass as we often did to the older horses. Instead, I sat quietly on my father's discarded jacket and singled out a handful of honey-sweet clovers to take back in the empty basket.

It was years before it dawned on me that, in those days of early childhood, many flowers would have been scarcely below eye level. My silent companions. To this day, it is always the flowers I remember. The incident may be half forgotten, shadowy. But never the time of year. There is always a flower confirming season.

Miriam, listening with patience to all this, said, 'Well now, since you speak of bacon... You are cordially invited to take breakfast with me.' I accepted without one moment's hesitation, for Miriam's billet is the envy of every Wren in Port. Indeed, there is an arm-long list of would-be successors, should her draft ever come through. We arrived hungry and cheerful at the neat villa, its surrounding garden ablaze with colour and spilling roses over the fence in welcome.

The two owner sisters greeted me warmly. Both were small and similar in appearance. Trim figures, rather bird-like bright eyes, kind, happy faces. Breakfast was set before us in a trice. And what a meal! Fruit, bacon, *two* eggs apiece, buttered toast, honey or marmalade. Coffee. Something quite out of this wartime world. Indeed, wartime apart, this household had about it an aura of Jane Austen.

The two ladies had obviously decided that their primary war effort was to be the care of their dear Miss Miriam Davies. To this end, they devoted much time and energy.

Miriam would return from night watch. At the click of the garden gate, the one lady would switch on the kettle and produce the welcoming cup of tea; whilst the sister upstairs would start the hot bath running. Half-an-hour later, an appetising breakfast was on the table. Upstairs, coverlets were being turned down and curtains drawn, beckoning their dear, exhausted Miss D to her sleep. Thereafter, a hushed silence pervaded the household as the two ladies tip-toed about their domestic duties.

Can you wonder that the waiting list grows?

Anna

HMS NEMO
July 1941

Dear James

I have now got an addition to the picture gallery on my wall. I will expand and set the scene for you.

Tess knocked on my door and came in.

'Do you like the surprise?' she asked.

'Well, I am only this minute back from duty and have just discovered it on my table.' I studied the photo more closely. 'Oh yes, surely it is you. A bit more severe perhaps, with your hair taken up from the collar.' The collar? I was puzzled. 'But the uniforms have not come in yet.'

Tess' face blushed with guilt. 'Anna, I was going to tell you but I wanted it to be a surprise. It *is* a nice surprise, is it not?'

Slowly, understanding began to dawn.

'You mean to say this is *my* uniform?'

'Anna, just the jacket, shirt and tie. And I only wore them in the studio. There wasn't time to ask. You were on duty.'

I spoke sternly. 'For your information, this particular uniform suit was made to my measurements by my Father's tailor up in Yorkshire. This is my Number One, not any old Service issue, thrown at me in a kitting-out session.'

'Oh Anna. Are you really angry? You will keep the photo?'

'More dumbfounded than angry, I think. But yes, I will keep the photograph and stick it up here in a central position; if only to remind me to keep my eye on what belongs to me. And anyhow, I know that you did not go to these lengths for me but for that love-lorn Canadian dancing partner. Now, is not that the truth?'

'Well, "Scorcher" has been pestering me for a photo in my uniform. He may be posted overseas at any moment. I couldn't disappoint him. Now, could I?' But brightening immediately, 'I shall give it to him when we go to the races next week. *Do* come. There's going to be a whole party with my sister and her husband and lots more.'

'No thanks. I should like to see Chief's face if I requested a day off to go to the Cambridgeshire.'

However, shortly after this conversation and upon the Wren Officer's orders, Chief *did* have to excuse me from duty one morning for the whole of two hours and was characteristically grumpy.

Apparently six Wrens had an invitation to play tennis with Marine Sergeants based on the other side of the estuary.

'Bring racquets and shoes when you come on duty in the morning,' were the orders.

We moaned at not having the chance to change into proper tennis gear but the novelty of the situation far out-weighed our vanity on this point. We were all pretty apprehensive as to their standard of play and fearful that ours might not come anywhere near it.

It dawned a glorious morning. Blue sky, blue water with scarcely a ripple. The launch, manned by two Marine Corporals, was waiting at the jetty. There was a definite air of adventure in all this, since normally the jetty was out of bounds, was wired off and guarded. However, today the sentry had obviously had his orders. With a broad wink, he stood aside and let us through.

We knew nothing about what lay on the opposite side. A seemingly endless stretch of fenland dominated by just the one feature, a Martello Tower. A sort of windmill without sails. An example of historic monument, I had thought. That it was indeed occupied at this moment, and by Royal Marines, was something of a surprise. Our cross-water trip was all too short. We landed, and from then on everything moved at the double.

To begin with, we were confronted not by grass but *hard* courts. This was something of a shock and in addition, *all* the sergeants were at least six feet tall! We discarded jackets, rolled up our sleeves, thrust cold feet into tennis shoes and in shaky silence, picked up our racquets. Pairing off was accomplished with parade-ground precision.

The first awful moments were spent in warding off the blows, so to speak, and getting used to the *pace*. Then, battle really commenced. We were on our toes. We were enjoying it enormously. It just did not last long enough.

The manners of our hosts were impeccable. They came down to the boat to see us off and on the way I saw, through scrubby grasses which grew everywhere on those sandy dunes, flowers! Brilliant exotic colours, short-stemmed and so totally unexpected in this setting. And I could not recognise any one of them. I scrambled in their direction, leaping over stones and low sand dunes and picked a great handful. Deep yellow, poppy scarlet, a blue so intense as to be indescribable, and a strange fish-like pink. Exquisite!

There were shouts from the boat.

'Come on!' they yelled. 'You're holding everything up. The *tide*, the tide won't wait for you. Come *on.*'

I arrived at the boat, breathless and apologetic and clutching my prize. We cast off, calling out our thanks and hopes for an early return game on our side of the water.

It was about a week later. In the office, just Chief and myself. Petty Officers busy elsewhere. I was totally immersed in the Gangway Sheets, the intricacies of which, I had mastered under the guidance of the POs.

This was real Naval stuff. One felt undeniably awed by the knowledge that this system and the same printed sheets had never changed their pattern since Nelson's day - Men Victualled In or Checked Out and whether they were T.T., Grog or UA (under age).

I was musing on this and on the fact that our own Head of Department, Paymaster Captain Nelson (Rtd but now returned for the duration as Commander), is indeed a direct descendant of Horatio himself.

Meantime, someone had come into the office and was asking Chief's permission, I did not catch the rest but caught a somewhat grudging 'Granted' from Chief.

The caller came over and paused beside my chair, casting a long, long shadow. A dark green beret, held over one hand, was lifted slowly, carefully and something was placed upon my desk. A brilliant posy, beautifully arranged and bound with grasses. I gasped in surprise and delight and looked up - a long, long way up, so it seemed, to recognise one of the tallest of the Marine sergeants.

Under the very trim fair moustache, the corners of his mouth were twitch-

ing with suppressed laughter and the blue eyes
danced with amusement.

'Oh, thank you.
Thank you.' I said. 'They're
beautiful!' He was gone. I
held the flowers up to my
face but Chief was grumpy.
He swung round in his chair
and glowered across to-
wards me.

'You should never
sniff them things, Miss,' he
said. 'I knew of a young
woman who did just that

and got insects up her nose and into her brain. She ended up in the asylum.'

I ignored this nonsense but decided to take my posy back to the billet at
the end of the morning.

Alas, for our hope of a return tennis match. We learned that very afternoon that the Marines were already on their way overseas!

Well, I can always press a couple of flowers!

Anna

HMS NEMO
August 1941

Dear James

Did I mention our First Aid class? I think not.

Far back in the winter, I decided to make enquiries with the idea of brush-
ing up on the subject. I had obtained a Certificate in First Aid at the outbreak of
war and had helped to start a class in our village. But all that seemed far away
and long ago. I needed a refresher course.

So, I made my way to Sick Bay to investigate the possibilities and was
completely stunned to find the whole outfit is run by men. Not a VAD. Not a
starched apron or wide muslin halo in sight. What, I mused, would be the fate
of a sick Wren?

However the MO told me I would be welcome to join the newly-formed
Wrens First Aid Class, meeting one evening per week. All were immensely dedicated and learned about administering morphia in a dire emergency and lifting
of floating bodies from the water.

One night, near the end of our session, the MO was called out to such an emergency. 'We will clear up and lock up and turn in the keys,' we assured him. The MO and his Chief, both already in oilskins, were halfway to the exit, bags and torches in their hands. Black night swallowed them. One of our members spoke up. 'Now then, why aren't we along o' them?'

She was a local girl. I had noted her quick movements, her confident way of tackling any problem in our tests. Of medium height, small featured, round face which never lost its summer tan. Deep set, dark brown eyes, keen and burnished like lamps in a lighthouse. Though her hands appeared slim, one only had to be bandaged by them to appreciate their surprising strength.

She spoke again, 'All this here practising. There's gotta be something at the end o' this.'

'Surely,' we agreed. 'Well,' she said, 'One Sick Bay Attendant, he lives in our road and I'm going to make a start on him. And you,' she said, looking around our circle, 'can tackle MO and anyone else with an interest. Anyone who'll listen. We're aiming for a trained team an' a rota. Two or three at a time to go out to sea as part of the rescue crew.'

Asking around, I learned that this Wren came from local stock. Father, grandfather and great grandfather had in their generation been coxswain of the lifeboat. Brothers and cousins had figured in the crew. 'She can handle a boat as well as any of them,' I am told.

Meantime...back to First Aid

There was to be a real live opportunity for those keen to earn their badges and for one and all to show their skills. For a big Combined Services Exercise, covering the whole county, was sprung upon us. First Aid Posts were to be manned at various points and ours came within this area. Speculation was rife; nervous anticipation in varying degrees was gripping each one of us. Only the MO seemed breezily confident.

The day dawned. A broiling Sunday in the middle of a seemingly endless heat wave.

We reported to Sick Bay; hair scraped back from our tense features, nails scrubbed till finger ends were red and smarting, shoes luminous with polish.

MO helped us into his spare starched gowns. I was completely engulfed and wondered if it would be possible to move my arms in any direction. The hem of this garment swept the floor.

Somehow, the necessary adjustments being made, I became mobile and we all queued up ready for action. We waited and waited.

'Maybe the Battalion has been wiped out,' someone suggested in a whisper.

'Get ready to deal with corpses,' giggled another.

It was unbelievably and unbearably hot inside those gowns. Outside, the sun blazed down; beat straight down so it seemed. No shadows relieved that treeless area. At last…distant sounds of transport approaching, then engines being switched off. Our 'casualties' filed in, singly, slowly.

We were lined up and took them in turn as they came. And as they did so, all my practice and self-assurance suddenly retreated, melted into oblivion, forsook me. With a mind completely blank, I faced a podgy, red-faced, sandy-moustached Corporal. His eyes gleamed with a look reminiscent of a horse about to give me a sticky ride. I braced myself and unpinned the list of 'injuries' from his khaki back.

'What's the verdict, Jenny?' he enquired. 'I'm under orders to be help-less. I'm all yours.'

With sinking heart, I realised that splints and bandages were going to be the least of my problems. I started on the 'fractures' - wrist and ankle. Then a small flesh wound on the back of the neck.

'Shouldn't you be undoin' my tunic and listenin' to my heartbeats? It would maybe surprise you.'

'Nothing wrong with your pulse,' I said tersely.

'Is that all? Jenny, you're clever, you're observant. There must be something they've missed.'

'Maybe,' I said. 'A suspected fractured jaw.' I reached across to the table. 'I've got just the bandage for that!'

Anna

Dear James

Tess had a blazing row with the landlady's husband. I was not present, praise be! But, she being Irish, both should have had the sense to keep off politics.

Well, it took Tess but twenty-four hours with official permission, to find this new billet. I was not very happy to desert Mrs M, who had always done her best for us and I shall miss the children. On the other hand, we had for some time been invaded by several and various members of Mrs M's family who were suffering devastating air-raids on the North East coast. It never crossed our minds to complain about the overcrowding. Our situation was fortunate by comparison with their real plight. Now our departure must be something of a relief to them.

So, though but a stone's throw in distance, we are now installed in an obviously superior residential area; in one of six villas with their colourful, lavishly tended gardens and well maintained exteriors. Window panes gleam, attractive curtains move gently within open casements. An aura of orderliness and quiet prevails.

So, for good or ill and through Tessa's recent efforts we find ourselves adjusting to this new environment. Our villa belongs to a retired Detective Inspector and his wife, the Pyms. House and garden are their first priority; food and cooking of a consistently high standard.

We, in our turn, are making tremendous efforts to be more punctual for mealtimes, are only giving way to noisy mirth in our own rooms and behind closed doors and, in general, are striving to create a favourable first impression.

Our rooms are tastefully furnished, chintzy and spotlessly clean. Tess, with a dramatic gesture of humility, consigned to me the larger of the two. Not for nothing have we lived under the same roof.

'Thank you so much,' I said, 'but I will take the smaller room and every square inch of it.'

So, after a reasonable spell of somewhat nervous adjustment, we have come to consider that we may be acceptable and indeed accepted; though a degree of caution is deemed wise.

Then, with less than a day's warning, Tess was sent up the coast on relief duty for a fortnight. At the end of the first week, I received a postcard; a black and white photograph of the harbour. I turned it over. In Tess' large, squarish, erratic, but oh so clear hand, I read: 'Anna, this place is full of lovely men with beards and pipes. We must both put in for a transfer the moment I get back. Tons of love, Tess.'

I quailed inwardly. The Censor! I knew little about censorship but someone had said that all Wren letters, outgoing and incoming went through Wren Office. A haunting thought. For days thereafter, I stuck to my back lane on my way to duty, avoided open spaces and became generally furtive in movement. A face-to-face meeting with our Officer could not, I felt, be of any advantage to me at this particular time.

The weather changed suddenly overnight and we awoke on Tuesday to a steady downpour. It lasted until late afternoon. Rain pattering upon the flat roof of our office is an oddly unfamiliar sound after the prolonged heatwave. I walked back in the early evening; the earth rain-soaked and steamy; little pools had formed in hitherto unnoticed hollows. But the gardens looked happy.

No tennis, of course, but I had albeit reluctantly agreed to go with Merton-Evans, our number one Sports Queen, to a darts match.

'At "The Wild Duck" across the common,' she said. 'Since you don't know the way, I will meet you at this end by the notice board.'

We met and squelched along a short-cut path leading to the far side of the common. Just beyond the Church stands "The Wild Duck", ancient and well kept with roof of Norfolk reed thatch, mullioned windows and always bright flowers to the foreground.

Somewhat dim inside, due to the blackout regulations but we headed towards the noise. Immediately we were hailed as conquering heroes and over-whelmed by offers of drinks from all sides.

'A sherry. Thank you,' I said, thereby drawing shouts of protest.

'What! No rum, gin, vodka? Sherry's poor stuff for a Naval lass.'

'Sherry,' I repeated and got instant attention.

To my horror, I was understood to be a member of the team... a playing member. Certainly Merton had never thought to mention this fact to me, other-wise nothing would have induced me to accompany her. I knew not one thing about the game of darts. Now, I bullied Merton into a far, dim corner where hung a disused dartboard and made her instruct me in the basic procedure. 'You're OK,' she said. 'Just concentrate.'

So, I concentrated and whether it was a case of beginner's luck or just pure fluke, I aimed and scored like an inspired demon. Thus the score gap widened, our team reaching dizzy heights.

'Have another swig, Jenny.' The glass was pushed into my hand.

'You're doin' marvellous,' they said.

The score gap widened even more. We won hands down.

Now, the losing side starting an argument and all concentrating on a flash-back post-mortem, I backed into the shadows. There to my horror, I be-came aware of four untouched sherries awaiting me on the counter. But there was some-thing else. A large and spreading plant. Quietly, gently and one at a time, I secreted those four glasses under broad green leaves and equally quietly and gently, propelled my-self towards the dim, blacked-out exit.

Once outside, I found the path - well *a*

28

path. I could not be too sure. I was sure of only one thing, that I wished, in the shortest possible time to put an ever increasing distance between myself and "The Wild Duck". For the thought of arriving on the doorstep of our villa with any or, heaven forbid, the whole lot of those I had left behind me, was sufficient to goad me on. I just hoped that I was on the right path and cursed the black-out. There did seem to be an abundance of undergrowth which I had not noticed on our way over. I brushed up against squat thorns and there were boulders on the path. Well, perhaps it was not much of a path. But it had seemed perfectly straightforward with Merton-Evans. However, I was well clear of "The Duck" and not being followed. Perhaps they had not missed me yet. They were all undoubtedly pretty merry. Come to think of it, I was finding it none too easy to keep to the path. How many sherries had I consumed? There had never been a chance to check since my glass was propelled towards me by hands unrecognized, every time I scored high.

Aware that the worst was before me and not behind me, I entered the villa quietly but immediately was bidden to supper. Mumbling something about removing my hat, I went upstairs. There, I lay on the bed and stared at the centre light above me. It was revolving, steadily and relentlessly. Round, round and round again. I groaned. Mrs P was calling gently from the foot of the stairway. Now, why on earth had I not made some plausible excuse such as having had supper with Merton? Only too right I had. I descended the stairs cautiously, adjusted my chair equally cautiously and sat down. Tea was poured, food offered. 'Actually, Merton-Evans insisted on me joining her,' I explained carefully and truthfully. 'I will just take tea thank you.'

Now, it would not have taken a Detective Inspector, retired or even half senile, to smell a rat. But happily and mercifully this one had his mind on other things. Mr P sat at his bureau and excused himself from returning to the table. He was ordering seeds and plants for sowing this coming autumn in his allotment. The order must go in the next day. Mrs P was called across to give her approval of this and that. She too, excused herself and took a stool beside her husband.

I sat quietly surveying the table; looking at the glass butter dish with ornate cover. It contained a slab of something blue-ish green in colour. This could not be butter. But then again, it could not be anything else. Not with Mrs P. Oh, no! The butter in the butter dish every time in this household. I was fascinated, horrified. I sat very still but nothing changed. I sipped half of my tea, said 'Goodnight'. Still with caution and oh, so thankfully, I took to the stairs.

Next day I bumped into Merton.

'Whatever happened to you last night?' she asked. I told her.

'Well, you do not surely imagine there was only sherry in those glasses,' was all I got from her. 'I am putting you down for next week's return match. Yes?'

'Never, ever again,' I said.

Anna

Dear James

Tess is back, starry-eyed and sated with romance, pressing me to join her in trying for a transfer to HMS Teal. I will have none of it for already I have seen our Wren Officer and applied for a draft to Quarters.

I know that I can do the work and I know too that our days of free and easy existence here are surely numbered. The place is expanding and inevitably Wrens will be put into Quarters. Everyone is speculating on the possible location and of course rumours are rife, but mostly pretty wild and all unfounded. Actually, there is an empty property situated on The Green and on which I would place my bet. It has a good position, looks the right size and both house and garden are really attractive. But no, not for me. If I do live in Quarters, then I aim to be a member of Staff.

Meantime we make the most of these final days.

Not doing anything outrageous but hugging the sense of freedom while it may last. Playing tennis till the light fails and then strolling oh, so slowly back. Even taking a turn down the lane or across the common as dusk deepens into summer's half darkness.

The RN tennis tournament is just over. In the draw for partners, I got the Pay Lieutenant. Or rather he got *me!* And his disgust was barely concealed. I feel sure he had hoped for Merton, our star player. Or, failing that, the Captain's secretary. Nothing lower. To be lumbered with the humblest member of the Department must have been a considerable blow to his dignity.

For me, I just hoped that I might do reasonably well, if only to confound him! Surprisingly we came second and I, in addition to my share of the prize received a rather wintry smile and mumbled 'Well done'.

Days Later...

I am writing this in the train. Yes James, I am on my way to start a new chapter, namely to WRNS London Quarters in West Hampstead. I gather that they are desperately short-staffed and therefore you may not hear from me again for some long time. And, anyhow, if I put my mind to letter writing during this journey, I will not be tempted to fall into retrospective half sad musings. Or at any rate, willingly or no, share them with me.

True, of course, I hate leaving Tess and I shall miss her sorely. I shall miss the fascination of the marshes. The eternal dominance of the sky just spreading itself out, endlessly. Nothing poking up into it or shutting it out between the onlooker and that far horizon. I shall miss even Chief. For between us we seem to have established some sort of acceptance the one of the other; and of course the two Petty Officers who have been ever supportive and good friends. Then our Commander Nelson, small, wiry frame, keen blue eyes, needle sharp intellect. A fair replica of his famous ancestor. Put him into the dress of that day and he would claim instant recognition.

I shall ever remember a certain winter evening when I was alone in the office. There had been a nasty incident at sea and survivors were expected. Hearing a slight rumbling I peered through the window to see the gangling figure of Chief, holding aloft a flickering oil lantern, his free hand steadying a piled high load on a handcart - Sea boots, jerseys, stockings, duffel coats and a mountain of grey blankets.

All these being propelled at considerable speed by none other than our Commander Nelson.

Who else shall I miss? Miriam, undoubtedly, but her parents have a house in Hampstead and we plan to get together on her next leave.

Lastly, of course, The Enigma. But since I know so little, there is little to miss...not much beyond a pale shadow. Whenever he is ashore, we play tennis. I cannot recollect the first time but always he is waiting with two others. Some one of us spins a racquet and we choose sun or shade (but a bit more nautical it has to be East or West). And we play, he my partner always. No conversation beyond, 'Yours I think,' or 'Yes' or 'No' and the current score. After play we go on our several ways, mine very short since I live almost on the edge of the recreation grounds.

Tess finds all this deeply interesting; far more than I do. She will arrive off duty, bubbling with information.

'Your boy-oh is in.'

'I know' I reply. 'And he is not my boy-oh.'

'So you *know*, Anna. Anna, you are hiding things from me. You have been seeing him or he's written to you.'

'Steady on,' I reply. 'Written how, pray, from the wastes of those patrol waters? By carrier pigeon? Or maybe some trained sea-bird? Surely you were awakened by the tap of a beak on my window in the night watches? The Awful Albatross!' Here we dissolve into idiotic mirth and wilder imaginings.

At last…'Well, and how *do* you know?' asks Tess.

'I know because I know that 'The Sunset Cloud' is in, since I was handed her accounts this morning. I do not have to see people to know whether they are in or out; I know their movements through what turns up on my desk!'

Last week a minor bombshell was thrown into our happy calm. This in the guise of an Order to attend Church parade on the Sunday. A first timer, this one and we hope a last.

Master-at-Arms had us out and shouted and blasted our ears with commands until he was hoarse and increasingly despairing. We weren't used to this. Every Friday we mustered for pay and were given about ten minutes drill as a preliminary to that. Not even Master-at-Arms took these little weekly enactments very seriously. Now the pigeons were indeed coming home to roost.

The Sunday dawned. Tess being RC was excused any part in the Parade. She was given a duty at the Base and with a gleam in her eye, witnessed our not entirely co-ordinated start. We had pleaded successfully with our Wren Officer to be allowed to bring up the rear. So by the time we were through the village and halfway across the common, most of us were in step with the Company. Tess, all agog, demanded a full account of the morning's happenings. And more especially since she had seen Enigma in charge of some part of the Parade.

'Did he speak to you?'

'He spoke to everyone, since he read one of the Lessons.'

'What else?'

'Well, he sang in the choir and assisted at the Collection.'

'Did he read well?'

'Yes, very well. I have decided he is a Cambridge man.'

So that was that and I got on with my packing and preparations for departure. Tess all moans. And the day dawned, today in fact. I went down this morning and said 'Goodbye' to everyone at the Base. Then Tess and Miriam and even Deirdre turned up to see me to my train and carry suitcases.

We took the nearest way, through the recreation ground. Surprisingly, there was a cricket match in progress, Enigma bowling.

A fieldsman tossed the ball in to him. He took it, faced back as if to bowl then, seeing us, turned on his heel, ball still in hand and came across the field accompanying us to the far gate. Asked where I was going. I told him. Said he was going for his Commission in two weeks' time. Said 'Good Luck' and I said 'Good Luck'. He turned and strolled back to continue the game of cricket.

Extraordinary!

Do write soon. It will help to dispel the strangeness. By the time I write again, I may be able to say whether this is a crazy move or one worthwhile.

Anna

HMS PEMBROKE
LONDON
November 1941

Dear James

Now is the winter of our discontent!

No looking back to the past golden summer. But since I have pitched myself into this slough of despond, I must set myself to enduring what cannot be altered, keeping a clear head and taking a long, slow look around me.

Our Quarters here are several adjoining houses in a long London terrace. Though still standing, they have not escaped blasts from nearby raids and scarcely a window or door fits properly.

In front of the houses, tiny neglected, square walled gardens border the Avenue. At the back, the basements open out onto a wilderness of weeds and erstwhile tennis courts; these bounded by the railway which at this very point, plunges from sight and becomes The Underground.

Transition from over to under, produces a roar, exactly that of a descending bomb. Quite nerve shattering, especially at dead of night. I am told one soon gets used to it.

Our office is a square room just inside the main entrance door. The disadvantages of being so immediately available are overwhelming.

As for office facilities, three of us share the one square centre table. A side each and the spare side accommodates the telephone. This instrument also serves Sick Bay, an unsatisfactory and sometimes highly embarrassing situation for both Sister and us.

The phone's other use is 'Emergencies'. Under this umbrella, our half-French VAD phones her all-French mother morning and afternoon to enquire if 'Darlingest, Sweetest Maman' is alive and well and likely to remain thus until her daughter's return in the evening. Showers of telephonic kisses conclude these touching interludes.

Needless to say, it is almost impossible, until the evening, to work with any measure of concentration. So, I tackle the mobile duties; checking lists, contacting people around the houses and since there are four flights of stairs to each house, this does give one a full if enforced measure of physical exercise (though even in Holloway they can exercise in the open).

These Quarters are sadly overcrowded; cold, shabby, comfortless. But being in London has many advantages to offset these privations. There's always somewhere to go, something doing, some friend or relation passing through with sufficient time for a meeting, maybe a meal.

Now there is a lull in the bombing, all are making the most of this respite. I learn that they have had their full share of deprivation here during the raids of last winter. All facilities, domestic and transport, cut off. For some, a six mile walk to duty each morning.

To my countrified eyes, there does still seem to be a film of grey over all. I cannot be sure whether it is dust from recent bombing or just a figment of my low-spirited imagination in present surroundings. Even our sky is rationed to small strips between roofs and chimney pots. Sunrise and sunset have no part here. They belong to happier places.

However, I think I have found an ally; one mature sharer of the desk. Her name is Berrington. She is a fund of reliable information on every facet of the set-up here. Seems to know everyone by name and I suspect, pretty well everything about them, though this she keeps to herself.

She has lived most of her life in India where her father was something connected with railways. Her chief interests are horse-riding and breeding bull-dogs. This last amounting past hobby to lifelong passion.

Only once have I accompanied her on a quick shopping expedition. She needed gloves. Woollen and navy blue. We sought out the nearest large store. Gloves were proffered, examined minutely.

'Seem all right. What is the price?' enquired Berrington.

'Three and sixpence, Madam.'

'I'll give you two shillings,' was the astounding reply. The assistant, scarcely able to trust her hearing, repeated the price. Her customer repeated her offer. Stalemate.

'Berrington,' I muttered, 'You are not in India now, you simply cannot barter over this counter.'

'Very well, I will try somewhere else. Good afternoon.'

Luckily, our time was running out. We turned back and I gave my verdict.

'No more joint shopping expeditions.' I am not strong enough.

Suddenly my companion, without a word, left my side, dashed across the road and accosted a lady who was walking two bulldogs. A long conversation ensued. I dallied, praying that nothing untoward might come of this incident since I had barely recovered from the last.

I began to wonder if Berrington, having failed over the gloves could be having a go for one of the dogs. But she was alone when we joined up again.

'Does your doggy friend live in this area?' I asked. 'Friend? Never set eyes on her before. But I recognised that young dog. Out of Pepita Glorious by Pride of Shalimar.'

I listened, willing to show some interest since it was only the pedigree she was after. But I kept to my resolve that this would be our first and last shopping expedition together. I repeat, I am simply not strong enough.

I have joined the rifle club and this makes a very welcome mid-week diversion. Service transport collects eight of us and we jolt along to Wellington Barracks where an army Sergeant Major gives us instruction. In varying moods of despair or rejoicing, we bring back targets and display them over our bunks.

So far the Sergeant Major is a model of forbearance and encouragement and at times, hopeful of entering two, or on better days, even four of us in the Interservices Tournament next year. One who will surely get there is Murphy, the Irish middle-aged cook (officers). She is an absolute wonder with a rifle and the fact that she gets fighting drunk every Saturday night, in no way impairs her precision of aim on Wednesday afternoon.

Berrington, learning that I pine for music, has found a source of complimentary tickets. She tells me she only likes military bands but I am welcome to take these tickets for the Albert Hall Sunday Afternoon Concerts. These, through her cousin Adrian (someone high up in The War Office). Thus, Adrian's batman arrives at our entrance every Saturday morning, asks for Wren Berrington and delivers the ticket.

I do not mind working in the office all Sunday morning, knowing that 2.30pm will find me settling myself on an excellently positioned plush seat with an afternoon of delight before me.

In some small way, I am able to return thanks for my pleasure. This week Berrington is suffering one of her recurring bouts of Malaria, a consequence of life in India. But there are complications, non-medical. Berrington fears she may be invalided out of the Service on medical grounds if these attacks come to light. So a discreet cover-up is under way; occupants of her cabin being sworn to secrecy and myself detailed to providing a constant supply of hot milk.

35

The sufferer, sweating and shivering in turn, tosses in her bunk, where she lies completely obscured in a giant sheepskin-lined sleeping bag. Meantime, I make circuitous routes to the galley at those times I know the staff will be off duty.

Arriving there by stealthy stops and starts, I dodge my way to the enormous refrigerator, extract a milk bottle, seize a saucepan, light the gas, heat the milk, turn off the gas, fill the thermos, wash and replace the pan in the exact position in which I found it. Now put the bottle in the empties crate, check and re-check that nothing has been disturbed.

Secreting the thermos under a sheet of official looking papers (stores lists and menus and the like) which seem a plausible alibi in case of any untoward encounter, I start upon my return journey, finally reaching Number Four cabin on Frobisher deck, deliver the life-saving beverage and feel thankful I never lived in India.

There is fog outside.

My spirits match the gloom!

Anna

HMS PEMBROKE
January 1942

Dear James

Suddenly, I felt the pull of the woods at home and opted for Christmas leave. About half the personnel went and the remainder (including *all* from over the Border, of course) took the New Year.

It was hardly a surprise that this one turned out to be but a dim reflection of former family Christmases. Just one sister and myself of our generation and the old house strangely quiet and empty.

We walked in the woods, sadly, a farewell exercise. The timber merchants had already moved in and every mature tree bears the arrow carved into its bark. The birds! We panicked for the birds. What is to happen when they come back in the springtime? No warning of this devastation, this blitz on their territory. They will become refugees in some other wood I suppose. But will they ever come back?

The timber wagons pass the house. Six powerful well-matched horses in burnished harness. But behind them their long burden. A funeral procession of forest kings. I was ready to come back to London.

Berrington, returned from a Malaria-free sojourn with relations in Hove, was also ready to plunge into work, that is, preparing our end of year audit.

So, New Year's Eve found us beavering away in the office. Not another soul in sight or sound to be heard; practically all personnel taking full advantage of extra late passes as befitted the occasion.

At last, I closed my ledger with a thunderous clap saying, 'Well GOODBYE to all that!'

Berrington continued muttering over her papers and some mysterious marginal scribblings.

'Look, Berrington,' I said. 'I have finished my lot. Let me give you a hand.'

'Thank you, but I have my pride,' came the rather terse reply.

'Well for once, just scupper your pride and let's call it a year,' I wheedled.

'I am certain that we can hit the balance this side of midnight.'

'No thank you. I have achieved the balance. There only remains the conversion.'

'Conversion? Conversion?' I queried and then came the astonishing reply.

'Yes, from rupees to £sd. I always work in rupees. So much easier. It's the conversion which takes the time.'

'Do you mean that you always do your accounting by this method?'

'Always,' she said.

I was speechless.

Just approaching midnight, our Officer poked her head round the door. 'We are just going Ma'am,' we assured her.

'Oh, no! not before the New Year has been given its traditional greeting. Come along to the Wardroom.'

There was a small gathering of Officers. They welcomed us and thus, full glasses in hand, we toasted in another unpredictable year.

Three days later...

This morning there was a ceremony enacted in perhaps the least ceremonious setting in Naval history. Seven Wrens lined up in one of our shabby, inadequate recreation rooms. Too mean a place to be designated Fo'c'sle but somehow attaining for a few fleeting moments, a strange brief touch of dignity and to me, even glamour as we received our promotion to Leading Wren.

We rushed off to sew the coveted anchor on the left upper sleeve of our jackets and all hastily scribbled a letter home with our news and would they *please* put 'L/Wren' on all future letters.

Well, I have got my anchor; the audit went off without a hitch, indeed even provoked a congratulatory noise from Chatham.

And Berrington had something up her sleeve, I could sense it. But it was *days* before we got the office to ourselves for a brief half hour. Then, out it came.

'Tyler,' she said, 'I have an earth-shattering disclosure for your ears alone.

Absolutely Top Secret. Even the Officers don't know.'

'Tell me, tell me,' I implored. I did not ask if she was sure because I well knew the source of her information. She was sure all right.

'Tyler, we are going to move. And we are getting something really good. The whole of the Charing Cross Hospital is moving into the country for safety and we, *we* are to have their nurses' quarters. At the first opportunity, you and I, my dear Tyler, are going to treat ourselves to a preview from the outside.'

But we had to wait for the right moment. It came when, under the guise of visiting a sick Wren, we left for the hospital, bearing chocolates and flowers. These we delivered and stayed by the bedside for the allotted span but returned by a strangely circuitous route.

Half-an-hour later found us standing on a pavement, and looking directly across the wide road to our future Quarters on the other side of it.

Scarcely trusting our eyesight, we leaned back against a supporting wall, slapping each other on the shoulder, whooping softly under our breath and probably looking less than sober.

I said, 'Buckingham Palace isn't a patch on this! I can't believe it. I just can't believe it!'

We gaped at the huge impressive edifice. Four storeys, red brick, white paint and in mint condition, displayed before us.

Nurses came and went through the wide doorway; my imagination transferring them into Wren uniform. Wrens with a real classy Establishment; with a huge fo'c'sle; with small quiet rooms for writing. Maybe even a Library. Certainly, large, airy galleys and organised, spacious messing. Minimum instead of maximum bunks in each cabin. Berrington and I would see to that.

This move was going to be the most terrific, most glorious operation; equalled only by that of the Children of Israel through their desert and into their Promised Land.

With rising spirits...

Anna

HMS PEMBROKE
Englands Lane
LONDON
March 1942

Dear James

We are installed. We are in our new home. But the manner of installation, the unbelievable giant hiccup of that operation has never been explained.

38

To put the thing in a nutshell, *we* moved in but *they* did not move out. Not for four days.

Just one wing was empty and there we existed as best we could, the rest of the building barred against us whilst the Charing Cross Matron and her nurses held sway with unbelievable tenacity.

We had just about sufficient floor space for sleeping with our mattresses laid side by side in the empty rooms and end to end, even along the corridors. In a far corner, one small naked gas ring, the only cooking facility, was instantly commandeered by Matron (*our* Matron) for sole use in her makeshift Sick Bay. All personnel were issued with Meal Tickets and sent off to find their three meals per day how and where they could.

To our department fell the daily task of writing, stamping and issuing several hundreds of these vital slips of paper.

I converted a wide step at the turn of a staircase into my 'Office'. It had its limitations but leaving aside the bathrooms, every square inch of every floor was given over to mattresses...

Inevitably, any mobility on our part, took the form of leap-frogging from one occasional gap between them to the next, since walking was an impossibility.

To an outsider - had there been any outsiders - we would have looked very odd. Beings suffering from some form of muscular dementia.

There were no outsiders. Only we insiders simply and solely engrossed in immediate problems. And there were plenty of those.

No one moaned. A sleepy, cheerful acceptance prevailed. We could wait. We counted the hours in silent, stoical, hopeful anticipation.

One week later...

The great machine is working on oiled wheels. Yes, we have taken over. Everyone has warmth, space and facilities beyond our wildest dreams. *Lifts* to all floors!

Our new office is tucked away some distance from the main entrance; thus only those callers whose errand is genuine, knock upon our door.

In truth, it is a somewhat dark and gloomy room but spacious enough for Berrington and myself. Our window faces North across a courtyard and directly onto the boiler houses. Not the most inspiring aspect, but I quickly discovered that by moving my desk to the centre of the room, I get the uninterrupted view of a very fine sycamore; and as I explained to Berrington, this keeps me in touch with nature. Berrington considers me to be in some way very odd on this count.

She and I are now in charge of cabin allocation. We regard this as being an exercise in psychology and derive great interest and a measure of success in teaming the matching personalities together. I marvel at Berrington's insight

39

and shrewdness, though I had always felt she was in the wrong category.

For myself, I have wheedled the Wren Officer into giving me permission to have a single cabin on the top floor of this building. That floor is currently out of bounds, considered unsafe in the event of raids. But I have undertaken to fly downstairs at the first wail of a siren and I am oh, so happily installed up there. It took several preliminary excursions to find the one room which, because of its size and odd shape, could not hold more than one bed and due to the slope of the roof, it has to be a single decker. I am safe in the essential requirements.

My dormer window looks east across the rooftops to the river and Greenwich. That pleases me.

Anna

Englands Lane
March-April

Dear James

We had snow last week. My rooftop view wonderfully transformed overnight; street sounds soft-pedalled; this lone cabin becoming my igloo.

Away down at ground level, a situation less romantic. Snow turning into slush and murky rivulets following in the wake of traffic.

Thus on the first bright afternoon, I announced to Berrington that I felt an urge to get my feet onto virgin snow and would she guard the office; or did she wish to come?

'You go,' she said. 'And good luck to you. All I crave right now is to get my feet into the dust of India. I could almost welcome a mild attack of sunstroke.' She pulled her desk closer to the radiator and toasted her hands.

In these new Quarters, we are more or less adjacent to Hampstead with The Heath but a short bus ride from our door and up The Hill. The sun shone. The air up there was sharp and clear. I struck off across the open towards a wood. Not a human footmark except the ones I left behind me. Plenty of recognizable indentations; large and small birds, rabbits, the odd hare and surely a fox, for I am almost certain that was his track, running in a dead straight line, with the occasional slight smudge where his brush had disturbed the snow.

Hazel catkins dangled in a hedgerow and just within my reach. I gathered a handful of twigs for my cabin, then turned back towards the sound of traffic, rather faint beyond an area of sizeable houses and tree-lined avenues.

A few hundred yards before the main street, a cobbled side alley claimed my attention. I turned into the opening and discovered a teashop with original bow windows, a climbing rose about them. Irresistible! In less than no time, a small rosy-cheeked body with sprigged apron was serving me tea and muffins beside a real fire. A young girl with flaming red hair was clearing a recently vacated table. There were china dogs on the high mantle shelf; a grandfather clock ticked quietly in an alcove. Enchanting! If Tupman, Snodgrass etc, had come in at that moment demanding a dish of tea, well  it would have been no surprise. Sadly, my time was running out. I paid the modest charge, closed the door with its tinkling bell and sped for the main street and my bus; the past dragging at my heels, the present urging me to get back to Quarters before daylight gave out.

The next time I went on the Heath, I could not find that teashop. Had I dreamed it? Had I strayed into the past on that afternoon? But the muffins had been real enough.

The catkins in my cabin are sheer delight. They can stay until the leaves come out and herald in the spring.

Last week we had photographers in Quarters in search of illustrations for a book on THE WRNS which is due to be published in the autumn. We were briefed and the day came. Everything, so far as we could judge, was shipshape. Corridors shining, galleys the customary hives of orderly activity; Berrington, (legally for once) opening the Canteen at an unscheduled hour and staging a little knot of customers.

Sister 'phoned me on the intercom. Would I go to Sick Bay. Now what on earth could Sister want? What possible hitch could have occurred in her Department? Emergencies were their business, anyway.

I hurried along. All seemed calm, bright and settled. Sister immaculate, sitting writing at her desk. VAD, holding a spoon and medicine bottle, was beaming at the world in general. Her golden curls were perfect under the whiter than white halo of her headdress, its red cross oh, so accurately centred.

41

'Now, where would you like to stand Leading Wren, facing the camera or profile? Yes, I think sideways would be best. Shall we rehearse?' And, glancing at the wall clock, 'They won't be here for five minutes at least.'

In some understandable stupefaction, I asked, 'What is all this about? Rehearse what?'

'The photographer. Surely you know about the photographer?' Sister now, and speaking with some irritation. I guessed that for one morning at least, her strict routine had gone out of the window.

'I know there's a photographer on his way,' I said. 'But what can I do for you?'

'Exactly this, you are our model, sweetie,' purred VAD. I heard this in total disbelief, followed by instant reaction.

'I am sorry but you can find someone else. Some other guinea pig. I am going straight to the Wren Officer Quarters for an explanation.'

I went. 'Ma'am,' I said. 'This business of photography in Sick Bay. I have never suffered one hour's sickness in my Service life. Never one dose, bandage or tablet. Except for a polite 'Good morning, sir', never a word spoken to the MO, Ma'am. I am sorry and I am ready to accept any punishment for this but I cannot go down to posterity with a physic spoon in my mouth.' She laughed in astonishment.

'Do you really feel so strongly about this? It was never an order; just a suggestion from Sister. But at this late hour, it must be for you to find a substitute.'

I soon found one. She was new to the Service, dazzlingly pretty and suitably nervous of doing anything wrong.

'You are to be photographed,' I said. 'Come this way, please. We are running it rather fine.'

At the door of Sick Bay, I knocked, piloted my victim towards the desk.

'Your model, Sister.'

I did not wait for a reply.

Anna

HMS PEMBROKE
Englands Lane
LONDON
May - June 1942

Dear James

It does seem an age since last I wrote but you can put it down to never ending work, since we are expanding at the rate of knots.

I have serious fears for my glorious isolation on the top deck. An invasion cannot be far away.

We are into early summer now. Lilacs and laburnums hang over garden fences. Even Berrington is willing to be dragged out of doors. We have discovered a café half way up the hill and on the best days, take off in that direction during our lunch break. Tables are set out on a wide pavement, continental fashion. We are served perhaps a fresh green salad with rye bread or maybe cheese rolls and coffee. Slender trees in tubs stand in-between the tables and on especially lovely days, a woman plays a Welsh harp by the doorway.

Other good news: Some inspired neighbour has offered the use of his/her garden, less than five minutes walk from Quarters. It is one of four in a wide cul-de-sac just off the hill. All these private dwellings are shuttered and closed for the duration. About this particular one, an ancient and very bent gardener does his best to quell the weeds and keep the lawns trim. But climbing roses of every hue and glorious scent are taking over everywhere, especially about the roomy octagonal summer house which is my chosen haven.

Here is shade or sun, according to one's preference. A wide fixed seat runs around the interior and a movable table makes an excellent desk.

I make the most strenuous efforts to snatch the odd couple of hours to take my work up there. Berrington has no wish to join me; she says it is far too much trouble. Moving house, or office, or even an armful of books, would be a sickening reminder of our recent move into Quarters.

Last week I got a surprise telephone call from Miriam. She is on leave and would I go to dinner, 7pm on Friday? Actually, their house is but three bus stops up the hill from the end of our road.

We talked in Miriam's room, exchanging news and covering lost ground, then went down to meet her father, mother and beautiful elder sister.

One of the highlights of the meal was a magnificent gooseberry dumpling on a beautiful old china dish. Miriam made a dramatic entrance, bearing aloft this fine example of culinary art, immediately reminding me of a picture in my nursery rhyme book, the pie with four and twenty blackbirds being set before the king. However, our gooseberries picked that day and sent up from their garden in the country, were a tender green, with a fresh sharp flavour and were served with country cream, and certainly having the edge on black-

birds! On the Sunday morning we met again and had a long walk on the Heath. We watched a shepherd and dogs rounding up sheep. There are acres of open grazing up there. I wondered how they manage without fences.

As I said, the work here continues to increase and a new, more senior Officer has been appointed. Under her control I, for one, find myself pushed out into hitherto uncharted waters and expected to keep afloat and on course.

At times her style and efficiency leave me quite astounded. For I have yet to meet anyone else who can, whilst holding the receiver of the telephone in the left hand, sign a succession of cheques with the right, whilst conversing.

Between pauses she will be dictating a highly technical letter to her writer and just to keep the ball rolling so to speak, issue a few explicit orders to me as I hover in the background.

Meantime I continue to enjoy the Sunday afternoon concerts by courtesy of Berrington's cousin and on two or three occasions have accompanied B to hear a Military Band Sunday Evening Concert in St James' Park. Berrington says she only enjoys military music so I enjoy her pleasure. And there are always the ducks!

Some days later...

Quite suddenly and without a whisper of warning, my present world is coming to an abrupt halt! For yesterday, I was summoned before this new Quarters Officer and told that she has recommended me for a Commission and I am to leave for OTC in two weeks' time.

Well, my feelings are in a jumbled state just now but doubtless I shall get myself sorted out. I hate the thought of leaving many friends here, especially Berrington and the work pattern we have built up together. And it will almost certainly mean leaving London.

Fearful of the severity of the course and being for three whole weeks under relentless scrutiny and assessment...

But for some consolation, being in Greenwich again and dining in the 'Painted Hall' (always a secret ambition).

So...nervous and nostalgic are the immediate moods. Do please write a word of bright encouragement in this my hour of transition!

Anna

Dear James

There has been no time to write until this last moment since our daily dose of lectures had to be written up and handed in within a very strict time limit.

Indeed, time limits are the overall pattern of life here. One is given, or allowed, so many minutes to get from A to B; so many minutes between each lecture; so *few* to fly across vast areas and scramble into games or gym kit in readiness for further exertion.

Nevertheless, it is entirely satisfying to be back in Greenwich, this time in conventional sleeping quarters instead of the vaults and to be eating our meals within the glorious surroundings of the Painted Hall.

Only Sundays here are quiet days, since some cadets go off on 36 hour passes. It seemed a good day to entertain, so I got in touch with my sister who is working in London, and with Berrington and arranged for them to come out on Sunday afternoon. We planned for them to join me on my last weekend in London and to this end, met to inspect a Services club run by nuns and recommended by friends. It stands on the edge of a very quiet tree-lined road. We were welcomed and shown around by a smiling, softly-spoken nun. The single rooms with pale-washed walls were simply furnished. The beds had coverlets of hand sewn patchwork. It looked good. We booked, then proceeded to the college in broiling heat. By the time dinner was over, it was cool, especially by the river. We wandered about the grounds, reluctant to hail the departure bus. I waved them off and pondered on the many hurdles to be overcome before our weekend of promising peace.

Hurdle number one, the Drill Test. Now, since those airy-fairy performances in HMS Nemo, any sort of drill has faded from my picture. Life in London Quarters allowed no time for it and since we were bounded on all sides by busy London roads there were no facilities in our neighbourhood. There had been, during all those months, but one opportunity in this field, a recruiting drive in the form of a Combined Services March, scheduled to start at the Fulham Barracks one Saturday afternoon.

Volunteers were called for and I was one of them. How could I have been so crazy? The day came. We leapt out of our transport at the appointed hour and place and were drilled into position by an unknown but simply stunning young Third Officer WRNS with a film-star face and figure to match. This, we felt to be a distinct advantage, since all eyes would be on our Leader and *our* shortcomings might pass unobserved. We started off on that six-mile round march on London's hardest pavements; which by the fifth mile had become without doubt the World's Hardest Pavements.

However, at the initial drumbeat, the first blast of brass, heads and hearts were high as we swung our way into the music. For three miles or more, all went smartly. Thereafter, whenever the band took breathing space and music stopped, heads drooped within the ranks; muscles sagged, the swing shortened in arms becoming increasingly limp.

Then, at the very point where this march threatened to fall into a stumble, the first recovering drumbeat and upsurge of brass entered into sagging limbs. With chins up, arms swinging in fine rhythm, we were urged forward.

'Left, Right. Left, Right.' Oh agonizing Left, excruciating Right! Shall we ever make it? Can we possibly last out?

We could and we did. And in the weeks that followed, our letters from home confirmed that cinemas up and down the country had us on their News Reel.

But back to Greenwich. No film cameras here. Just the Marine Sergeant, erect, correct and eagle-eyed. Each day he selects a victim and puts her in charge of the squad. Inevitably my turn came. Sergeant gave me the route. I manoeuvred my group together and into line and started into the march. So far, so good, but then, so help me! I barked 'Right turn!' when it should have been 'Left turn' - and marched them towards a high stone wall.

Miserably, I knew that only sudden and immediate death could get me out of this impasse. Practical solutions fled, speech fled and something else…the coveted tricorne, in my imagination, was now rising upwards, floating away 'till it became but a speck disappearing behind a black cloud.

In the end, I cannot remember whether it was Sergeant or I who gave the releasing command - 'About turn and forwards march!' - to my victims who were still stoically marking time in front of the stone wall, expecting almost anything. I cannot imagine any vocal rescue being offered so must conclude that my voice was back from flight. We were on course or so I thought, when Sergeant loomed up rather suddenly, fixed a strange look in my direction and said, 'You will cut out the river path this morning. Take them to the Observatory.' I guess a solid stone wall is one thing but a wide stretch of the Thames, well, that could be different.

The next hurdle, the Principal's tea party. Throughout the course, approximately eight cadets were invited to make up the daily party, in order alphabetical, in reality somewhat nerve-shattering. Here, social standing, ability and accomplishment are under surveillance. I felt invisible most of the time and got the impression that my presence passed virtually unnoticed.

However, surprisingly good marks from the lecturers have elevated the sinking morale in some measure and I find that two or three kindred spirits are sharing my fluctuating moods over this course. We foregather at coffee break and balance the ups versus the downs.

Against any of these, we have experienced one splendid occasion which I must recount to you in full.

It was during breakfast one morning, my neighbour said, 'Have you noticed anything?' I shook my head. 'No? Well you just keep your eyes skinned,' was her advice.

I took my usual fresh-air-before-lecture walk without any eye skinning, noticed trilby hats and long mackintoshes, their wearers standing around in doorways, at crossroads, two by the river gates. In the afternoon they had not left us. I gathered from the shaking of heads, the raising of eyebrows that we weren't supposed to notice anything.

This was ridiculous. If anyone wished to escape notice within these precincts he must be in uniform, never mind what form it might take. Yeoman of the Guard, Fancy Dress, plenty of buttons and a peaked cap of sorts would suffice. But civilian garb invited the footlights, whereas a couple or so of Admirals would be neither here nor there.

Came the dusk and the mystery men had increased in number, especially around the river gate. Someone was expected and that 'someone' was coming by river.

By the time we had trooped into dinner, the cat was out of the bag. Winston Churchill and the top Naval brass of America were dining here. Menu:- Lobster Soup, followed by Roast Duck etc. Our Principal had been invited to sit with them on the dais, their only lady guest.

We stood as they came in and were seated. I don't think any one of us noticed what *we* ate. Whenever possible, heads were turned in the direction of the dramatic scene. The Yanks have a far more theatrical weight of gold braid than *our* chaps. For that one night at least, that dais became a glittering stage.

We cadets were reluctant to move off to coffee in our own Quarters. It seemed an anti-climax indeed. But within half an hour, a message came through. Mr Churchill had gazed around the gun room and asked, 'But where are the Ladies? We must have the Ladies.' The 'Ladies' needed no second bidding. We dashed helter-skelter across the campus to arrive somewhat breathless. We circulated in a happy informal atmosphere. A young officer played the piano. Oh dear! It was no concert grand, but after a couple of opening bars, any shortcomings were completely drowned in riotous song.

A Churchillian selected programme almost entirely of fourteen-eighteen favourites. For him, I guess, there had never been the time nor the opportunity to learn our current editions. But tonight was a time to relax. He smoked the cigar, or thrust it forward to emphasize a point to the weightiest of surrounding circle of brass; then turning towards a group of us by the piano, commanded "Tell him to play Tipperary, we will have Tipperary!' 'Yes SIR' we yelled above the songsters. But we did contrive to sandwich in a few of our own current favourites.

Next day we were told that our guest on thanking the Principal, had told her that the evening had been his first experience of relaxation since the war began.

Meantime, no relaxation in *our* midst. We had arrived at the crucial moment when we were to appear before the Selection Board. Our Judgement Day. The waiting period outside that dark forbidding door. At one moment it seemed too long, at the next not nearly long enough, for at any second one's name would be called. The Board Room was dark and gloomy. About six senior Wren Officers sat in a row on the far side of a heavy mahogany table. Not one of them smiled.

'Sit down Tyler,' said their spokeswoman. The questions began. They seemed to be looking for someone, a cross between a Games Mistress, a Guide Captain or a Girl's Club Leader. I was none of those.

'What games do you play?'

Completely forgetting HMS Nemo and our hockey coaching under the International Star and again my oft-times tennis partner the thrice County Champion, rather dully, I just said 'Hockey and Tennis'.

The atmosphere was altogether unsympathetic. The questions bored into one; the answers received in an aura of suspicion. Maybe they had read the drill sergeant's report. Surely they were thinking, 'Well, she doesn't know left from right. Not much of a leader. Too uncertain. *Basically uncertain* (not good in an Officer).'

Another question: 'Should you be given a Commission, have you any preference as to location?'

My answer, 'My home is in Yorkshire, Ma'am.'

Covert looks passing from one inquisitor to the next all down the line. A few scribbled notes shuffled and reshuffled. Slight nods of acquiescence. Then their spokeswoman, 'You will report as Third Officer Quarters to Plymouth next Monday.' So much for my preference!

James, one day...we will celebrate...

Anna

HMS DRAKE
PLYMOUTH
September 1942

Dear James

I do realise that weeks have passed since you received my last letter, despatched from London on the day of my departure for Plymouth.

A gloriously sunny morning and, if you remember, I had just spent that weekend with my sister and Berrington. They left for duty at an early hour on the Monday. I saw them off then took a walk in St James' Park. It was there that I received and returned my first salute! Strange, it sticks in the memory, a landmark, the starting post, if you like of my Commissioned career.

On that afternoon, I boarded the train for Plymouth; since when, I have had not the least inclination to write. This longest silence should have given me time to get my bearings and form some sort of life and work pattern.

Not so! Over the weeks here, I have not settled into anything, since there would seem nowhere in which to settle - no niche to fill - no task crying out to be tackled. Our particular WRNS Quarters have the name Hyperion and are situated in an area of large Victorian family houses occupying the high northern outskirts of the city so far distant from it as to have lost any feeling of affinity with the sea.

Sullen, brooding yew and cypress trees surround us and take up more than a fair share of garden space and the lawns and flowerbeds, though kept tidy, seem to have lost heart since their rightful owners went away.

Nevertheless, this seclusion has proved a heaven-sent haven at the time of the great and devastating blitz upon the City. Resident owners had moved to safer areas and in their place, the shops and offices have taken over here. In many cases, a whole terrace will belong to one department store with number 1 the shoe department, number 2 haberdashery, number 3 glass and china and so on.

Down in the City, on the seafront, where once thrived the hotels, the offices, the shopping centres, there is nothing. Nothing above ground level higher than two bricks, marking, in outline, their original foundations. A life size map, if you like, pencilled in brick and stone. There are no people walking there and no stray dogs. It is eerily silent and very tidy.

But back to Quarters, if I *must*, for I am not so far enjoying the life here. The inside of these houses proves to be as depressing as the exterior. The Victorian era prevails. Dark wallpapers and paintwork. Turkey carpets, heavy velvet curtains and huge mirrors reflecting and doubling the prevailing gloom. Our office is a vast room. OIC, her telephone on the huge mahogany desk, occupies a large leather swivel chair in the bay window. Chief Wren, her ample form spread before a slightly less imposing desk, guards the entrance door.

I am allocated a smallish table with one shallow, inadequate drawer and an extension from the aforesaid telephone. Here I sit signing hundreds of meal tickets, since most of the Wren personnel work away at the Naval Base, Docks or Shipyards and feed at the various canteens. In order to procure a meal, the official ticket must be surrendered. Papers of secondary importance are piled into my in-tray for signature.

The main Wren Officers' Mess is the next house adjoining our garden. In the course of some official paper signing sorties, I have met several of the younger ones. They are friendly and socially inclined. One of them took me on a spectacular bus ride along the coast. We had tea at a country manor house looking out to sea. They were busy harvesting their huge apple crop, helped by two ancient gardeners and on Saturdays, the bigger lads from the village school.

There is a very pleasant club for Naval Officers on the Hoe where I dine on my one free half day per week. Here is quiet welcome, good food and service above most wartime standards. The large windows look directly across the Hoe and far out to sea.

Should I augment my single glass of wine by one or two (or more), I feel certain that the faint click of wood on wood and surely a slight haze of tobacco smoke would not be far away, as I stroll across the historic grass and linger 'till last light.

Two Weeks Later...

Quite out of the blue, I have been put in charge of a smallish Quarters across a main road about ten minutes walk from here. Their officer has gone sick and is not expected back.

This is a stone house, ivy clad, many gabled and aptly called 'Ivydene'. It borders the road but has gardens on three sides.

So, I am getting to know my staff and at least to recognise the personnel who leave each morning and return in the evening or vice-versa as many do night-watches.

I am occupied making a list of improvements to be tackled in order to make the place more comfortable and attractive. We could do with bigger rooms but I have discovered an attic running the whole length of the building. This will make a splendid recreation room for table-tennis and drama and dancing.

I mulled all this over for several days and then had a surprise visit from Superintendent. I liked her instantly. She is down-to-earth and encouraging and has promised materials for curtains and covers for the shabbier chairs. Also table tennis equipment and more library books. I called a Mess meeting and got 100% volunteers for the planned renovations.

About three days after all that, I was summoned before my former Officer at Hyperion and told that I was being sent on leave and given my rail ticket for the following day.

I was astounded. I had not put in for leave, did not want leave and had far too much on hand at this particular moment.

Well, mine not to question why. Perhaps for some very good reason, the leave rota had to be changed. I supposed that my plans could be shelved for seven days.

So, I went off the next day and whisked around the family with half my mind in Plymouth still.

The return journey took a whole long weary day. A taxi awaited me at the blacked-out station, the driver saying he was instructed to take me to Hyperion. I arrived, somewhat puzzled and in darkness. Then it was the bomb fell. My particular bomb. I was re-appointed to Hyperion. Another Officer was already installed in my place at Ivydene.

To add to the confusion, a dance was in progress in a huge marquee erected in the field behind Hyperion. Everyone, with the exception of two sentries was dancing there. I tidied myself up and went in the direction of the music, hoping I might there find some friend who could enlighten me. There was a brilliant full moon over the field but little illumination inside the marquee. I leaned against a guy-rope in a daze of disbelief.

'Care to dance?'

My inclination was to reply: 'Not really. To die would suit me better, right now.'

But we danced and he was amusing and I put my horrors aside for a couple of hours. We sat on a stile in the moonlight and he told me about Norway, his country, and the snow and the mountains. He was a mountaineer and a national ski champion and desperately homesick.

Afterwards, we walked up and down in the middle of the road in the moonlight, he talking, I listening, pushing the nightmare of this new situation out of sight for the moment. There was little sleep for me in the short night that was left.

I awoke next morning with the expectation of an explanation. None was forthcoming. Once again I was back at my inadequate table desk, signing meal tickets.

My friends next door were pretty outraged and sympathetic but quite unable to enlighten me.

'Cheer up' they said. 'It's a well-established jumping off position for new young officers. You will not be there very much longer.'

They were going to a tea dance given by an Army Regiment in barracks just along the road. These dances were a Sunday afternoon institution and we had a standing invitation. Thus, a party of us walked the short distance towards the sound of music.

It was a very large wooden building and the band remarkably good.

'May I have this dance?'

He was tall with sandy hair, a small trim moustache and the bluest eyes with a distinct twinkle in them. The music started.

'Oh good,' I said. 'It's a waltz. I'm old-fashioned. I like waltzing.'

He threw back his head and roared with laughter. After that we danced all the time.

Apparently there are Saturday night dances at the only large hotel still standing in the town. I had heard of these from my fellow officers. Would I go? Surely I would. My partner was on duty until 2030 hours, but I would arrange to go with friends and my partner would be in the foyer of the hotel at 2040 hours.

On the following Friday, OIC summoned me with news that I was to leave for Dartmouth next day. Their Quarters Officer had gone on sick leave and I was to stand in for her. I felt suddenly very brave and detached. Could I report on Sunday instead? I had a date for Saturday evening. The astounded reply was swift and to the point. 'Indeed NO.'

My appointment was from Saturday, therefore I must report on that day. What to do now? I asked myself. Somehow I must let my poor would-be dancing partner know. And here it was suddenly borne in upon me that I knew neither his name nor his Regiment. But he *had* said he was the Signals Officer.

I requested time off to pack and immediately rushed off to the makeshift Post Office, housed in a cottage among some trees beyond our kitchen garden. Here I found a sympathetic Postmistress and explained my immediate predicament.

She said there were TWO Regiments in barracks just now. Could I remember anything about the badge on his shoulder? Not a thing. But I plumped for the Queens Own something or other, and together Postmistress and I concocted:

'The Signals Officer Queens Own etc...

Please phone this number...URGENT' giving our office number.

A few hours later, as I cleared my desk, the office phone rang and was answered by OIC. 'It is for you, Third Officer.'

I picked up my receiver and was greeted by a hoot of laughter from the other end. My mysterious telegram, since it was addressed to The Signals Officer of the Regiment, had been treated as Official and Confidential.

Since the said Officer was out on Exercises, a despatch rider had been sent off to deliver it thirty miles distant. Well, when that hilarity had died down, I delivered my message in no uncertain terms.

Thus we said what both agreed was a very unsatisfactory and quite unnecessary farewell.

So...after all that has gone before in these past weeks, I can say with certainty that I am not building up any hopes of Dartmouth but just approaching it in low gear till I see what lies around the corner.

So, James please write...
c/o WRNS Officers' Mess, HMS Dartmouth, Devon.

Anna

HMS DARTMOUTH
October 1942

Dear James

It was quite dark when my train from Plymouth stopped in Kingswear Station. There was a lot of movement on the platform but I sat on in my corner until a porter poked his head through the doorway.

'Kingswear, Miss,' he said.

'I'm going to Dartmouth.'

'Well, you won't get there by sitting still,' he said. 'You takes the steamer now and goes across the river. There ain't no more railway. Best hurry, Miss, there ain't no more steamers neither, this side o'mornin'.'

Somehow I got myself and baggage aboard in almost total blackout.

It was but a short trip. A shadowy figure, obviously on the lookout, spotted and rescued me as I stepped ashore. Sharing out the baggage, we walked the short distance to Officers Quarters.

Several days later...

James, this place is a picture postcard come to life. The river opening into the sea, steep banks, wooded on the eastern side (I haven't been over since leaving that train).

On this side, shops by the waterfront, then many small hotels dotted away seawards towards the Castle and the Point. Secluded houses in their gardens spread upwards away from the shops. Crowning this rise and completely dominating all, stands the Royal Naval College. The College is Dartmouth. Dartmouth is the College.

The Wren Officers are quartered in a rather fascinating many-gabled house with stucco ceilings, oak-panelled walls and strange Old Testament Biblical scenes in plaster relief above the open chimney pieces.

My office has a galaxy of stars on the ceiling but I am spared the antics of bearded Prophets; and it is a lovely room with a deep-silled window running the length of one wall and affording an expansive view of the river.

There would appear to be close liaison between Wrens and College, for this house is almost entirely and very comfortably furnished on loans from Up There. I have an imposing desk (Commanders!) and a distinctly choice mahogany tallboy. My bed fits into an alcove behind the door and two easy chairs beside the gas fire complete the picture.

Within this establishment, almost all the residents are watchkeepers. At any time of day or night there are the sleepers, the newly awakened, those coming off Watch and dropping their weary forms into the nearest armchair. Meantime, others are angling their tricornes, seizing gloves and shoulder bags ready to step it out up the hill to where duty awaits them.

As for me, I am endeavouring to assimilate my duties as best I can, since there is no one to hand them over to me.

The first essential is to find my way around, geographically and to get to know the Quarters personnel. To this end, I set out each morning and do the rounds. It had not occurred to anyone to direct, let alone accompany me, on the initial excursion. I got my steward to point me to the nearest Quarters and so on from that one to the next. They are scattered around, up and down, the steep hillside. NEVER have I negotiated so many steps. My muscles are simply not attuned to this mode of exercise and I find it crippling and excruciatingly painful. It seems ridiculous for there are elderly residents of more than twice my age nipping nimbly up and down the hillside between front door and shopping precinct, carrying laden baskets and keeping up a spanking pace, not a twinge of agony on their bright, fresh faces. I can only suppose they were born to this.

In the course of Rounds the other day, I noticed an ill-fitting door on a wardrobe.

'Petty Officer,' I said. 'Is there something amiss with that door?' She reached forward, touched it and immediately it sprang open, releasing what I can best describe as a rainbow. A staggering display of turquoise taffeta, rose silk and cream lace billowed out of captivity. Small ermine jackets topped these confections, weighting hangers to rail.

I stared in disbelief, then learned that many Wrens had brothers, cousins, friends, among the College Cadets. There are frequent dances. The College has its own cinema with weekly programmes. I seem to have strayed into some high society social club!

All this was short lived. Cadets were evacuated from RN College to safer areas, the finery parcelled up and sent home and 'Uniform to be worn at all times' became the order of the day.

Anna

HMS DARTMOUTH
December 1942

Dear James

Bless you for your letter of hope and encouragement! You ask for news, well here it is:-

We are expanding rapidly in all directions and I am enjoying every moment of this life and pushing to the back of my mind the knowledge that I came here only on loan; and further, the post is now becoming one for a more senior Officer than I.

Mackenzie, a Third Officer in Operations here, has an urge to change over to Quarters. On her off-duty evenings, she comes into my office and helps me through the daunting back-log of paperwork, accumulated since my predecessor went sick. In addition, my daylight hours are spent on routine rounds plus the opening and equipping of a number of newly acquired houses, leaving only evenings for office work. Thus a helper is more than welcome. It is evident to me that this one would make a dedicated Quarters Officer.

So, with the minimum of fuss or palaver, the higher authorities have approved the change and Mac is now installed in one of those two large houses on that hilltop on the Kingswear side of the river. These form a part of the current expansion. I am now released from my daily Alpine ascent and the two ferry crossings. A considerable saving in energy and time. In return, I have guaranteed that Mac shall have her feet on Scotland's soil before midnight of December 31st in order to celebrate Hogmanay amongst her kinsfolk.

There is a deep and solemn meaning to these customs surrounding Hogmanay. As a mere Sassenach, I am not expected to appreciate any of this. But it will be my lot to sleep over the other side and take charge, since there is no access by river during the hours of darkness.

January 1943

Christmas here was quiet. About half the personnel on leave and we remaining Officers having Christmas Day to ourselves. The Officers Staff were sent off duty and we managed quite happily on meals prepared and left ready for us.

The 'Carving the Turkeys' rounds took up a large slice of middle day since it included some additional Quarters on this side plus two newly opened on the other side. But transport was available and all went well.

A wonderfully mild day and the more energetic of our mess went off for a long walk in the surrounding countryside.

Here I must recall that, 'On this Christmas Day afternoon, in the year of our Lord 1942, I did pluck from a Devon hedgerow bank, one wild strawberry, ripe and large, and did eat the same with much satisfaction.'

We had our Christmas dinner on Boxing Day and invited any young Naval Officers not on leave or on duty at that particular time.

December 31st found me over the river and toiling up that hill with hand-luggage at the start of my ten nights in charge. Since I must be on duty on the other side during the day, I have worked out that I shall cross this river twenty times come the day Mac's leave ends.

With practically no warning, a number of us were summoned to attend a three day course in Plymouth. I looked into my office on a final check to find two new young Third Officers standing there - one Admin, one *Quarters!*

There was no point in leaving them behind, so I said, 'Sort out hand luggage for three days and come to Plymouth. I will consult First Officer. Since she is coming, there will be no-one to show you the ropes'.

After that I lost sight of them for those three days. There were masses of Officers from the whole of the Command and the course was tough with lectures all morning, all afternoon and again after dinner.

I was anxious to get back to Dartmouth and find out more about this new young Officer. Indeed I was not certain which of the two *was* Quarters.

The course over, we awaited our transport in pouring rain, seeking some shelter under a thick hedge and disturbing a bird which flew out, dropping a splash of white on the sleeve of my raincoat. I reached for a large cleansing, rain soaked leaf, but First Officer said, 'Leave it. It might mean something. My lips are sealed.'

I felt confusion and apprehension. Were my days numbered?

Back to Dartmouth and sorting out the two new officers. My future helper is Third Officer March, the taller of the two. Round face, a wide smiling mouth, small features and a pleasing contralto voice. I guess she sings.

I was right about the voice, and oh, heaven be praised, she has a sense of humour! In addition, she has brought a typewriter and this eliminates the need for a Wren Writer. We share my office and everything that happens there.

Our fishmonger respectfully requested an audience. If he supplies the Wrens with fish, then his 'regulars' must go without. I told him to go ahead with his local customers. The Navy must look after us.

So, with a deal of correspondence and red tape twisting, a meeting was arranged. Three Ministry men in long raincoats and trilby hats were waiting in a small office on the Brixham waterfront. Why three?

I was alone - so battle commenced. Dartmouth was a separate area from Brixham etc. But we *had* Wrens in Brixham with newly opened Quarters and everyone knows there is an abundance of fish in this Brixham area. I used every argument. In the end I was promised written confirmation from THE MINISTRY. So, Thursday is to be the Fish Trip Day. We take a Brake down to the Brixham waterfront and meet the incoming Fleet.

These are Flemish fishermen, escaped from the Germans and bringing boats, wives and families to safety on this side of the water. They live in the many vacated cottages up and down the steep hillside around the harbour.

The boats with sails of royal blue, orange, scarlet and marigold make a glorious armada as they come in with the day's (or night's) catch. The men wear flat black caps or berets and black waders but their smocks are of that same brilliantly coloured sail cloth.

In contrast, winding their way down the steep hillside come the wives in long, dark, full skirts, black woollen shawls over their heads. They meet the incoming fleet and help with the sorting and boxing. Gutting and weighing is the men's duty.

I believe they suffered many losses before their escape. We Officers receive frequent gifts of crab or lobster along with our fish ration.

Amity reigns!

27th January...

James, I was just about to post this when my *promotion* came through. I am trying to believe it. The ghost of an alien 2/0 taking over is laid to rest.

Now we can forge ahead. I've got the best 3/0 there ever was as my assistant and the choicest people in the world with whom to work. So many new young Officers in our mess.

Where did all these lovely people come from?

Anna - 2/0

HMS DARTMOUTH
March 1943

Dear James

We, that is my Third Officer and I, are settling into a fairly organised routine and sharing the outside trips. These are increasing in number and variety, for in addition to visiting newly opened quarters to east and west along the coastline, we have incorporated two fresh vegetable collections.

An Army Colonel's wife grows tomatoes in her several greenhouses and we are assured of a regular weekly supply. In that same locality, we discovered also a farm/market garden growing acres of cauliflowers. Our order awaits us at the field gate. Both trips can be organised alongside the routine visit to our Salcombe Wrens. A considerable saving in time and petrol.

A new ship has taken over at the College and an astounding break with tradition is the fact that Wrens are part of the Ship's Company.

Came the morning of their arrival, February 13th, First Officer decided that she and I would pay a brief courtesy visit. We drove up the hill and found Wrens but no Wren Officers. There should have been two.

However wartime travel, by whatever means, is a dicey business. First

Officer would go off and make some enquiries. I would stay and organise and help with the unpacking of several crates which were arranged alongside the mess tables down the centre of a huge dining hall.

We were almost through to the last crate, when the sound of an approaching plane caught our attention.

No warning, so it must be one of ours.

Then...SWOOP...a steep dive downwards, followed by a dull thud. At that moment we also dived down under the tables. Mess traps trembled. Plane now tearing overhead towards the town. Two dives, two explosions, getaway plane gaining speed and height. Gunfire along the coast. The All Clear.

We emerged from what we realised had been a singularly questionable 'protection' - that is, a table piled high with several hundredweights of crockery and cutlery. But this was only part of the situation.

Behind our particular wing, about one hundred yards away in fact, stood a churned up mound of earth and, sticking up on top, a red flag. Two sentries finished wiring off the area and affixed a large notice - 'KEEP AWAY - UNEXPLODED BOMB'.

We located and posted a notice on the door of the Wrens' indoor shelter entrance and I left them to their lunch break of coffee and sandwiches. Cooks were to prepare an early high tea. Petty Officers would supervise allocation and making up of bunks. There were suitcases waiting to be unpacked. *No-one* was to set foot out of doors.

Down in the town there was considerable damage about the shopping centre. There were casualties and a large area was cordoned off.

Mercifully, all the Wrens' Quarters had escaped damage. But there was no sign or news of the two absent Wren Officers. Later, I packed an overnight case and walked up the hill.

A few more Wrens had arrived, completely exhausted by a day of chaos on the railways and not reassured by what they saw at the waterfront when disembarking from the ferry. There would be no more trains, no more ferries this side of morning.

59

Then the town siren and our own College siren wailed. We made for our shelter. A unique affair this, Naval Cadets written all over it...figuratively speaking. It was, in fact, a highly polished shute from ground floor to basement floor below.

One sat down at the top, let go of the handrails, and...hey presto...one's feet were on the ground. I wondered what the record number of Cadets per minute might be.

We could not hear very clearly what was happening in the town, but certainly there was gunfire. Presently...the All Clear.

Officer of the Watch requested a list - name and rank of all personnel.

So, once they were all in their bunks, Chief Wren and I started on what became a formidable exercise. I suppose it could have been funny if we had had any sense of humour left in us. We had none.

Our victims were all dead beat and mostly half asleep. Then came one who resisted all our attempts. Chief looked across the bunk to me for guidance.

'Turn her over and read the name tape on her pyjamas collar,' I suggested. It worked - thus all ensuing difficulties were solved.

It was morning.

A steward was standing there with a cup of tea.

The bedside phone was ringing. Duty Officer reporting that the Bomb Disposal Squad had been and all was well.

I descended the spiral staircase towards my bathroom. Halfway down, a high narrow window looked out onto the Admiral's garden... There was a lawn with slender young trees and at their feet, short daffodils, their heads moving, gently, happily.

That moment will remain with me to the end of my life.

Anna

HMS DARTMOUTH
May 1943

Dear James

Sorry. James, for this long delay.

We have been madly busy and barely had noticed that Spring is with us and the coast and countryside are miraculously beautiful.

However, it was in a mood sadly at odds with all this that found me toiling up the hill on a mission; in essence, to lodge a complaint. This matter could, I felt, have been dealt with far more diplomatically and I had no part in it. I tried rehearsing my opening gambit but with little success. The content was highly explosive, however I might try to dampen it down.

I knocked on the door of the Surgery. 'Come in'. I obeyed and faced the Port's Irish Medical Officer. Poker-faced, I delivered the message and waited for the ensuing explosion. None came.

Instead, a slightly bemused tone. 'Sure. it's as plain as Murphy's donkey where that message came from. Sit down, sit down.'

He posted the 'Surgery Closed' notice on the outer side of the door, unlocked a small corner cupboard and brought out a bottle of Irish Whiskey and two glasses.

We talked. As Port Medical Officer, it was one of his duties to inspect any new Wren Quarters. Had we not just opened such a one along the coast at Beer?

Yes, our furthest Eastern outpost in fact.

We would take a trip out there. One day next week. He would borrow the Captain's Official car. We decided on the day. I descended the hill, light of heart and foot.

Thus, on the most perfect of May mornings and not wishing to delay the trip, I waited by our street entrance. No sign of the Captain's car, but a short way down the hill was parked a very small ambulance. Out of the driver's seat was clambering an instantly recognisable figure.

'And the top o' the morning to ye, Anna,' he called, waving his cap.

All staff cars were needed for a High Rank meeting in Plymouth. But sure wouldn't we have the broth of a view from this added height? I agreed we had the perfect vehicle for our trip. Thus we cruised along those Devon roads between hedges of hawthorn, covered white with their scented blossom and bowed with the weight of it.

We sang. A lot of Irish songs. I just la-la-la'd when I wasn't familiar with the words. We arrived at the village and leaned over a half door to watch the world famous lace-makers plying their intricately beautiful trade.

From thence to a splendid lunch at the nearby Inn. The sea was a wide

61

bay of deep blue below us and the cliff tops and sandy roadsides were ablaze with golden gorse.

We reached the house which was the Wrens Quarters. The Petty Officer in charge greeted us in a small central hall; flowers giving a welcoming touch and everywhere gleaming with polish.

But there was something. A space. This was not quite an ordinary entrance hall. I gave a second exploratory look. There were no uprights below the handrail on the staircase, just a yawning great gap.

PO explained. This house had previously been occupied by a Commando Company awaiting embarkation. Commandos are not allowed fuel except for cooking. It was winter. Consequently, my Wrens were deprived of banisters, shelving of any sort (in or out of cupboards) and lavatory seats. PMO produced a notebook and entered this illuminating information, promising it should receive First Priority.

There followed a routine inspection of Quarters, which indeed confirmed all we had been told.

After that, tea and delicious cake. Farewells and our homeward journey. The sun still shone.

We never stop working but the variety is limitless!

Anna

HMS DARTMOUTH
June 1943

Dear James

Sunday afternoons, now the weather is right, are given to sailing.

First Officer of the College has put a Cadets' cutter into use and has issued an invitation to us Wren Officers to spend our afternoons sailing up river. We meet at the jetty and take turns with the College to provide the picnic tea.

There is an excellent mooring spot round two bends and about half a mile away from habitation. Here, we disembark at a sandy inlet on the edge of woodland and make a small fire. If all available fallen firewood should be sodden from recent rains we head for the nearest dwelling in the depth of that woodland and ring the rear doorbell. It is answered by a Naval AB who takes and boils the kettle in no time at all.

I am fascinated to learn that this house, currently on loan to the Royal Navy, belongs to Agatha Christie!

But back to the river…

All are expected to do their part in the manning of the boat. I, for one, realised very early, that I knew absolutely nothing about sailing.

Somehow, managing to back away from the initial teething troubles, I realised that there was one piece of equipment which was plain to recognise and unmistakable, being the only one. This was the Centreboard. Central and in truth, a board. An added bonus being that it had but two positions, Up or Down. Therefore, but two commands could be issued, ie, 'UP Centreboard' or 'DOWN Centreboard'. No funny angles or degrees or Naval gobbledegook could apply in this case.

So, once it became clear to me that the command actually meant what it said, I ensconced myself in the correct position and left the manning of jib, mains'l or tops'l to anyone sufficiently experienced or sufficiently rash enough to take the upping or downing, the tightening or slackening thereof and, not least, to risk being shouted at, should they err in any direction.

On the return trip, just occasionally, we are becalmed at the second bend in the river. Fate seems to have taken the wind out of those sails, indeed seems to have taken the wind out of the world.

Time is running out on some of us.

It may be Sunday afternoon but at least half a dozen of our party will be heading for duty in less than an hour from now. However, every eventuality has been provided for. An MTB is there, just around that bend and doing nothing in particular, just lolling about (or whatever may be the nautical term) in the water. But on a second glance we see there is an AB in charge.

In a trice we are lashed alongside, MTB's engines running smoothly and we reached the jetty with time to spare.

Later...

About two weeks ago, duty rounds took me to what I believe will be the WRNS Dartmouth's final Eastward boundary. The journey there entailed leaving our brake on the north side of a wide estuary. There, a motor launch, manned by a Chief PO and two Ratings, awaited our arrival at the small jetty.

The opposite bank of this estuary was low and wooded. In the one clearing stood a large house with gardens and lawns running down to the water's edge. That I learned was our goal.

But there was one unusual feature in this typical woodland and river picture. Protruding several feet above water level were metal rods, resembling giant walking sticks. Some type of tide-measuring equipment perhaps? That was my silent thought.

'Would you care to steer Ma'am?' asked Chief.

'Oh, thank you, yes Chief,' was my instant reply. 'That is if you will provide the necessary guidance.'

'That is my intention, Ma'am, since we are crossing between minefields. Keep her in the path between these posts.'

So I concentrated on Chief's quietly spoken instructions such as 'Keep her to port now' or 'gently, gently, to starb'd'.

Since James, you are receiving the remainder of this story, you will conclude that the crossings were achieved without incident.

The new Wren's Quarters (until recently a Girls' Boarding School) has a superb position. But under present circumstances, an oddly deceptive picture of perfect peace!

Annual Leaves are starting. This involves switching personnel to fill temporary gaps and extra monitoring. There will be less time for letter writing from this end, but I hope this will not deter the occasional written word from your hand!

So, overworked and undermanned...

Anna

HMS DARTMOUTH
January 1944

Dear James

Thank you, thank you for the lovely Christmas mail. I am really sorry that I could not manage more than the card but Chief Officer was called away to some distant place in Scotland. A telegram. It read, 'Auntie's condition deteriorating in Rosyth Hospital. Imperative you visit her immediately.'

So here was the vital information...time and place of her Naval Commander husband's arrival on Christmas leave! With our blessings and good wishes, we waved her off on that long and joyful journey. I seem to be left to organise our Christmas!

For some time, a plan had been formulating in my mind. The Wrens would go Carol singing, not round the houses but round the ships on the Dart.

I approached the Vicar, who is also Hon Chaplain to Naval personnel here. He and his wife are dedicated musicians and good friends to all Service personnel.

The Vicarage is open house to us at any time. There, we are welcome to play their grand piano, the choice selection of gramophone records; write letters, read, or just enjoy the garden.

But back to Christmas...

My idea got instant support and that meant one excellent tenor voice and the almost certain addition of an Army Major from RE's Mess round the bend in the river. He is a powerful bass. There remained the crucial hurdle, namely, obtaining permission to take a boat out after daylight. Everything hinged on this. The moon being at the *full*, saved the situation. We would manage without lights.

So, came the night; silent and clear and still. Not a breath of wind. We gripped torches and Carol books, got aboard then made upstream to the first victim of a surprise VOCAL ATTACK!

Waterborne, the voices took on a new dimension, indescribable. As we visited each ship, the crews rushed up on deck, some struggling into jerseys over their pyjamas! We were hailed on arrival and cheered on departure to the end of the line.

Approaching the waterfront, we were amazed to see a huge crowd of the town's residents, taking up the strains of what had been intended as our final item. Not so! There and then began a second and vastly augmented choral performance. Never had we imagined that our modest carolling at the bend up-river would end in such grand operatic style.

The incident took pride of place in the following week's edition of the local newspaper. And - much more important to us - was mentioned in every sailor's home letter as being the highlight of Christmas.

Happy New Year!

I wonder how you spent it!

Here we entertained the American Officers on New Year's Eve. Flaming pudding ceremoniously borne in at midnight. Plenty of singing, some rather limited dancing from one room to the next across the landing. *They* showed no sign of fatigue. *We* were distinctly showing signs of near exhaustion. It threatened to be an all-night session.

At last! Some move in the homeward direction...or so I thought, and shook some hands in farewell...or so I thought...

I must be getting tired. Surely we had never invited quite so many...Now, that dark fellow with the very unusual and obviously American pince-nez. Did he have a twin brother? Identical? Surely I should have noticed this. Then...the truth dawned. They were departing through the main door, skirting round the building and re-appearing through a side entrance!

I alerted one of us and within five minutes the game was foiled. No comment from either side! We shot the bolt and staggered off to our short sleep.

Next day, over lunch we were busy giving vent to the unanimous feelings, punctuated by groans of fatigue, when I was summoned to the door. There I found three coloured American Stewards, their arms laden with gifts from our guests of the previous evening. Cards thanking us for 'The GREAT PARTY'. Huge boxes of the most luxurious American chocolates, biscuits and other confectionery. Several bottles of Irish Whisky!! Coals of Fire, indeed!

Since none of us is very interested in drink, we shall now have to throw a party to the Brits.

Anna

HMS PEMBROKE
My new postal address...
Shelley House
Swan Walk
CHELSEA
May 1944

Dear James

Please note the above. I prefer to tell the story in those few bald facts. Yes, I have left my beloved Dartmouth.

And anyhow, the handing over of those Quarters and contents and staff, was no light matter. It concentrated the mind.

On my last evening, there was a Ratings Dance in progress at Warfleet, our latest and largest Quarters.

I watched from a balcony and then left by car accompanied by two friends who saw me off at midnight on a train. I was in London by daybreak.

The Quarters here occupy about eight houses on the Embankment; with our Officers Mess at the extreme west where the road branches off, strangely curving away and indeed could not be more aptly named. Our Wardroom window forms part of the neck-shape. It is on the first floor and we look directly across the road, and into the Physics Gar-

dens. Fascinating! Very old, bent garden-ers tend the plants; and weed and water and push wheelbarrows which look too heavy for them. I just long to explore that place but my request was refused. No visi-tors are allowed during wartime.

Our Officers' Quarters form part of this curving terrace and this particular house belonged to an artist, so I am in-formed. Certainly the owner of many pic-tures, for the deeper coloured shapes on most of the walls show where the paintings hung. All, we hear, have been evacuated to safety.

But back to the present. Each day, after lunch, ten minutes are devoted to 'Curtsey Practice'. Reason...Our Commandant, HRH the Duchess of Kent, is on the point of paying us a Visit of Inspection.

For me, I suddenly realised with horror that both my uniforms were quite unfit for the occasion. But the 'handing over' of books and equipment must be got through and I had no time to go prancing off to Harry Hall's, my service tailor. However, the firm had my measurements. I 'phoned and was promised delivery on time.

The package arrived by hand on the morning of HRH's visit. With shock and horror, I gazed at a tunic fashioned for someone twice my width. The skirt sloppy, but the *jacket!* It was HUGE...*preposterous*. It was not, and never had been intended for me.

What to do? I was faced with the miserable choice - either be downright threadbare and disgrace the occasion or cut a 'Bessie Bunter' figure.

To be threadbare would be an insult to our Royal President. I stood with the rest as we lined the pathway to our Quarters and made the much rehearsed curtseys. The ADC, Lady X, following HRH slackend her pace momentarily, turned her head in our direction and with a broad wink of a sky-blue eyelid, breathed 'Hello Girls!' Silently, I blessed her for that one brief moment of humour in the midst of my personal nightmare.

As Quarters Officer, it appeared to be my privilege to steer our guest towards tea in our Wardroom. Mounting the stairs, she smiled kindly and said 'Ah you are Henson.'

Now Henson was one of our young married Officers, in the seventh month of pregnancy and awaiting her much-delayed relief officer. I pulled myself together and in as even a voice as I could muster, said that I was the newly appointed Quarters Officer. My day was in ashes!

Our WRNS Sick Quarters are in Tite Street which branches off the Embankment just a few minutes walk from here. Nursing Sister tells me that her next-door neighbour is Augustus John, the famous artist. And more interesting, the fact that General Montgomery is currently having his portrait painted. He arrives by taxi at eight o'clock each morning. I was invited to a first-hand view and went off in good time to be positioned and briefed by Sister. It was an historic but amazingly brief occasion, since General Montgomery sprang from the taxi, straightened to his full height and was across the road and up the flight of steps in five seconds flat, to be perpetuated in colour.

Since our Nursing Sister is a fund of information on this locality, I asked her the whereabouts of the nearest Church. I want to go at 8am and be back in time for Sunday breakfast. The nearest I am told, is the Chelsea Pensioners Chapel, just along the road. Anyone is welcome there. Accordingly, I found it quickly and easily, though there were only a handful of civilian worshippers that Sunday.

The Pensioners occupied the choir stalls. I supposed it was sensible since a few were quite disabled. They were in full uniform and wore *rows* of medals which swung forward and rattled loudly on the pews as they kneeled. It sounded like harness...dray horses moving proudly round the show-ring came immediately to mind.

During the Epistle, I studied that remarkable congregation. Every one

of those faces a page of history. I wished and wished that I could draw.

The following Sunday, as I came within sight of the Pensioners Chapel, something appeared to be afoot. The old warriors were lined up on each side of the short flight of steps leading to the entrance.

It must be Church Parade or a special visitor who merited a Guard of Honour. I lingered by the shrubbery until the ceremony should be over. Nothing happened, no one arrived. I glanced at my watch. Only minutes to go. *Then* and only then was it somehow borne in upon me with stupefaction and total embarrassment, that the Guard of Honour was for me!

I hurried forward, gave my smartest salute and went up those steps at the double. This remarkable ceremony became routine. Not a word did I breathe to a soul.

Anna

HMS PEMBROKE
7 Swan Walk
CHELSEA
15 June 1944

James

For security reasons I have never been able to explain to you *why* I was sick and sad at leaving Dartmouth, especially at so crucial a time. So, here it comes...

Shortly after my appointment to Dartmouth - 'on loan' - I attended a *Top Level* meeting which outlined the immediate expansion of the Command. And you will recall my fears of being supplanted by a more senior officer; also my jubilation on being promoted and appointed to Dartmouth. This meant I would see my part through in this Programme. Well, I did see it through, except for the final act.

So far as the preparations were concerned, all was in readiness. The river was so full of waiting craft that the water was scarcely visible between them.

The waterfront was cut off behind barbed wire and guarded by Army sentries. To gain access when on duty, one had to show a pass. This operation entailed two salutes from the Sentry, accompanied each time by a thundering stamp of the Army boot. An unnerving experience ('till one became used to it).

But we are the Silent Service. No one spoke about what was going on under our noses.

We waited for The Day when we would be waving them off. And then no doubt, trooping across the road and into the Church and praying for them.

So come D-Day, you may know where *my mind* was firmly fixed.

I crossed the road here and gazed into waters of the London Thames and said the things I wanted to say to them. Firmly believing that some small, wayward, Heaven-guided current might be on its way to Normandy.

Anna

HMS PEMBROKE
7 Swan Walk
CHELSEA
July 1944

Dear James

Thank you, thank you for your letter coming from the deep countryside. More especially at this time of sudden and terrible turbulence which has so deeply affected each and every one of this community of Wrens.

Our First Officer was absent, or sick, leaving myself and the Admin 3/0, Margot, in charge 'till her return. As usual, I went to Early Service with the Chelsea pensioners. There were several air-raid alerts during the morning.

At about 2pm a message came through that two stewards had not reported for duty. Their Petty Officer came to me, worried about their non-appearance. I said that since there had been raids during the morning, it was possible that the Underground trains were affected.

Petty Officer said: that being the case, they would have started off to walk, however far. They had never been late on duty. Never.

Communications were disrupted but we continued to put out queries. Later, came the news that the Guards Chapel had received a direct hit during the Morning Service. Friends of our missing Wrens were almost sure it had been their intention to go to that particular service.

We 'phoned Headquarters WRNS who took over all responsibility for information. They would alert us immediately anything came through.

We sat up until the early hours. Switchboard were to wake us. Nothing came through.

Early on Monday morning an HQ voluntary driver came in an Admiralty car to collect Margot and myself. Information was that our two Wrens were thought to be among yesterday's casualties in the Guards Chapel. Both lived in London. We were to drive to their homes and inform their parents.

I cannot speak too highly of that driver. A war widow herself, she imparted help and guidance for the task confronting us both.

They left me at the gate of the first home and would collect me on their return journey. The gate opened onto a path between a wide flower border. There were flowers everywhere and sunshine. I cannot remember any sunshine indoors; it seemed different, with a deepening shadow over everything as I imparted my news to the stunned family.

The father wished to come with us to the Mortuary where we hoped to be given more definite information. We took him with us.

There was a wide crowded Information Room with a counter running from East to West, and behind the counter, very young surgeons with lists; answering questions and taking down names and answering more questions. Fatigue and the nature of their task had drawn all colour from their faces; their eyes had a frozen, unseeing expression. I do not wish to describe their coats. In the end, we were sent away, sympathetically and told there was still some 'tidying up' to be done. We would be informed.

Since our HQ car was due back at a given time, we took the bereaved father to the nearest underground station. It was terrible to see the stricken look on his face.

Margot and I, overwrought by the events of the morning, felt that we could not face lunchtime in the Mess. Our Petty Officer Steward brought us a tray in the Wardroom and that routine continued for all meals. I do not know what, if anything, we ate. I only recall water biscuits and whiskey. We were never hungry.

Tuesday found Margot and me boarding a bus on our way to a Church where all the dead had been taken. Unfortunately I could not recall the names of our two Wrens. The handing over of seven houses and contents had occupied my every moment, leaving little time for personal contact with anyone other than my predecessor, now urgently needed in her new appointment.

I was in no way qualified for this vital task of identification. So I waited by the Lych-gate on the Church path. After some time, Margot came out of the Church. She was crying. Remorse struck me. How *could* I have let her go alone?

'I don't know, I'm not sure,' she said miserably.

'Come,' I said and we turned back.

Fear of the unknown was gripping me.

The porch was in almost total darkness. We moved through into the

Church. There was no fear here. Only complete silence and
utter peace, the like of which I had never experienced. The
pews had been removed. On either side of the central
aisle lay the dead, in long rows. The tall Guardsmen
on the right and the other casualties on the left.

All were in shrouds of hessian.

The pale feet of the Guardsmen remained uncovered...'The feet of the
Disciples'...That bit of the Bible came into my
mind...'And washed the Disciples' feet'.

A long way forward, the blacked-out
East Window, a Cross and a small lighted candle in isolation. It was almost totally dark up
there ...shadowy. A mound of earth and a
spade...The Garden of Gethsemene? For a
moment - and then there was only darkness.
It had been imagination.

Our Wrens were side by side near the
centre aisle. I could not recollect ever seeing either of them. Margot said she
was now quite sure. They also wore identity discs. We replaced the covering
over their faces and left the stillness behind.

Petty Officer Wren Steward consulted me about the Funeral Parade. She
was calm and wonderful, choosing the Wrens who could be relied upon to show
no emotion. A Marine Sergeant came and we had a drill and slow march practice in a quiet road behind our Quarters. During the funeral there was an air-
raid warning as we stood beside the shared grave.

I came away feeling that I never again wished to hear a bugler sounding
the Last Post.

Margot and I have returned to meals in the Mess. First Officer is back in
harness. She contemplated putting in for a transfer to Eastbourne to be near
her infant son.

I have received a letter, from 3/0 March. She is being appointed to
Quarters at QUEEN'S GATE! We shall be NEIGHBOURS...give a few miles
more or less. I am trying to believe this piece of fortune after all that has happened since I set foot in London. We are planning...planning...planning.

Write soon

Anna

P.S I have received a lovely letter from the bereaved parents of one of
our Wrens. They ask me to visit them. *A.*

Dear James

Thank you for the quick reply and for your comforting letter.

Here, our new problem is, of course, the V-bombs, which do not penetrate so much as blast on the level. This means that we must sleep below ground-level and my Night Rounds have become the most vital part of Duty. Every Wren must be accounted for and listed before she closes her eyes for the night.

Promptly at 7pm, just as 'Workers Playtime' starts on the wireless, I start off, tin hat on head, notebook and pencil in hand and I list every person in each house, praying that the 'All Clear' will hold until I have completed the task.

Fortunately, all these houses on The Embankment have basements, which if you like, are ready-made shelters. Anyhow, there is no alternative and they have become dormitories.

Having completed my list, I hurry across The Embankment to where on a seat are two women Air Raid Wardens. To these I deliver the vital Lists. They spend every night on duty out there and have never missed one night since this war began. Muffled against the weather, torches, sandwiches and flasks beside them, they have become an institution, if you like. When, *when* this war is over, I hope they may receive a decoration. Certainly they will deserve one.

My sleeping pad is at the foot of a flight of stairs so that I can get to ground level without disturbing sleepers. After every nearby explosion, I grab torch, put on tin hat and go up to inspect my third of our Quarters. The other two thirds are receiving the attention of my two assistant Officers. We meet and confer before returning to our respective bunks. The Early Duty Watch is stirring by 5am and I am able to sleep, bath and get to the breakfast table by 9am. My two Third Officers catch up on *their* sleep during the afternoons.

For some reason my welfare has been taken over by Chief Cook. She appears at the door of Quarters Office about mid-afternoon, bearing tea and honey sandwiches. This honey is *special*. Not the nectar gathered by the bees, (impossible to obtain now). This is a wonderful recipe consisting of fresh parsley, sugar and water, boiled together until setting point is reached, and then strained into a jar. Looks like honey, tastes like honey and according to Chief, will 'keep me going'.

Third Officer March 'phoned me. She is now appointed to London, Queen's Gate Quarters, and is coming over on Sunday afternoon. I fear we shall not be spending our time in dissipation as planned, but it will be wonderful to see her.

These days one of my little problems is getting to the Bank. Hitherto, my weekly trip with the Canteen takings had been a routine job, fitted in at the Bank's opening hours and my convenience. No special day or time. All that has changed. I start out, immediately an All Clear is given, and hope and pray I may at least get to the bank with money and self intact. There are many deserted and damaged houses betwixt here and there. Most have basements with open or blown-out doors. I make mental notes as I hurry along with the money bags - notes of where to dive in a sudden emergency along the way. That is the positive side...

But back to 3/0 March. On Sunday afternoon she arrived, blue rings under her eyes, confirming lack of sleep - it had been a particularly noisy night. The adjoining cabin to mine was, I discovered, empty, so I borrowed the mattress, pillow and adequate covering and transferred them to a space on the floor of my cabin. My guest settled herself thankfully. I scrambled onto my resting pad and we exchanged news and gossip and arranged a meeting when, if ever, things outside our control should present the opportunity.

Early one morning, a V2 exploded across the river from us. The blast shattered a glass roof - a sort of central well in a basement galley.

By the time I got down there, surfaces were cleared of glass. Cooks, wearing tin hats, were busy cooking breakfast at the stoves. Mercifully, no one was injured. They had taken shelter in a pan cupboard under the stairs. But there were large, jagged pieces of glass resting precariously on the roof frame. Why had such an eventuality escaped the notice of the Safety Department? Or equally, MY notice? Repair and safety measures started immediately.

C-in-C London came very early next morning. I got practically no warning and had the quickest bath and dressing time, and no time at all for breakfast before his car was sighted and somehow we contrived a semblance of composure before he set foot on our doorstep.

At the end of the inspection, C-in-C asked if there was anything he could do to help personnel in this most difficult and dangerous time. I plucked up all my courage and said I thought that starting Leaves again would be the best morale booster, (all Service Leave in London had, for security reasons been stopped). Next day, the Order came; 'All Leave To Be Resumed.' Thank heaven it had been the right request and more important, had elicited the desired reply. The atmosphere lifted, visibly. Leave lists were organised, days were counted and re-counted. Farewells, returns, dates ringed on calendars. Now there was movement where there had been stagnation.

Meantime, the Service work that goes on here in Chelsea is in imminent danger owing to the unpredictability of these V2s. Therefore, we are *moving*.

Captain's Wren Officer Secretary and myself were sent north of the border. There were no sleepers on our night train so we dozed, fitfully. A dash of cold water on the face, a brief comb through the hair and a hopeful straightening of the tie, was all we could manage before alighting at our destination.

Admiral's car and chauffeur awaited us and we were whisked off on half-an-hour's journey to a waterside hotel of many windows overlooking the Estuary. Without warning, we were ushered into a dining room, where stood the Admiral himself.

'My wife and daughter will be down in a moment,' we were told, and turning to me, 'Porridge, Second Officer?'

Now, surely this must have been an entirely unique occasion. No one, truly no one except Alice in Wonderland could ever have been offered porridge by an Admiral. But I was able to reply, in a tone firm and steady - or so I hoped, 'Thank you, Sir'.

Captain's Secretary, now more forewarned, accepted her porridge gracefully. Then arrived the Admiral's ladies, wife and daughter, somewhat surprisingly introduced to us as 'Grousie' and 'Doodles'. So, we breakfasted there in that mostly glass-sided room, looking out across the estuary, with a tiny ghost of Lewis Carroll lurking and swinging invisibly among the glass chandeliers.

The rest of the day was, I fear, but bitter reality. Starting with the pick of the bunch...One small hotel by the waterfront and somewhat detached from the rest, which were two red brick Victorian houses on a hillside among other similar residences. They had stained glass windows on the staircase and one house possessed an early Victorian bathroom, the bath resembling a mahogany coffin! The lid, when opened, latched back to the wall by an iron hook and staple, revealed what had in another century, been a floral decoration but was now unrecognisable as a portrayal of nature, being faded, worn away, or deeply stained by the iron in the water. All equipment in this room was in a like state.

Now to the largest dwelling, a Hydro possessing a tall lookout tower with a small room at the top and a spiral staircase leading up from the ground floor. The Hydro was in two unequal parts, the larger being joined to the smaller by a spacious ballroom, underneath which were housed a sea-water heated swimming pool with sea water baths alongside.

This whole edifice was perched high on a wooded cliff with steps leading down to the estuary far below. The galley, with blacked-out glass roof was semi-basement and in an indescribable state of filth. A little old man with a guttering candle and a long iron poker was prodding around hopelessly in the semi darkness.

'What are you doing?' I asked, bravely, and fearfully awaiting the response. But I could have saved my breath. The reply came in such Border-Scots that I never understood a word of it. There were pantries off this cavern wherein were wooden sinks infested with cockroaches. This surely, was the final straw.

We spent that night at a Wren Officers' Quarters and left for London next day in a mood bordering on despair. It looked like a choice between V2s and cockroaches. That is, if it had been a choice. It was not.

We conferred as the train sped towards London and Chelsea. The LANDSCAPE, the ESTUARY, the HEATED SWIMMING POOL, the BALLROOM, the SAFETY of REMOTENESS. All these we would emphasize.

No mention to be made of *Isolation* of Remoteness, Private transport to Duty only, spasmodic Public Transport.

NO WORD OF COCKROACHES.

Anna

HMS COPRA*
Skelmorlie Hydro
Largs, Ayrshire
September 1944

Dear James

The days following our preliminary (and revealing!) excursion to Scotland were hectic.

THE MOVE

This must be planned as a campaign. I had ascertained the size and accommodation capacity of each of the four houses.

After appointing resident Quarters Staff, the rest of the cabin accommodation was available to Wrens' own choice, as near as possible, giving friends the chance to be together. Blank plans were posted for this purpose.

* COPRA ~ Combined Operations Pay and Ratings Allowances

Each of the four houses was given a different colour...

Blue for *Birkenward*   *Yellow* for *Strathclyde*

Green for *Craigevar*   *Red* for *The Hydro*

Two or more of these notices were posted in every house along the Chelsea Quarters and a luggage label in the designated *colour* tied there-on. Once the lists were complete, all personnel luggage labels were issued, named and affixed. After that, only the colour became relevant. We were to be met at Glasgow by separate transport for each of the four houses and all personnel and matching luggage collected and transported. The sorting of suitcases would be a simple matter, once the destination was reached.

So, the day (or night) of DEPARTURE came. We were to travel overnight, taking a picnic breakfast. The hour approaching midnight found us aboard for Glasgow on what we were told officially was the longest train ever to leave Euston Station.

It consisted of the entire Personnel - plus luggage of - Men and Wrens of the ship COPRA, the Quarters Staff, all the Ledgers, desks and Office equipment. The Wrens' mess tables, five pianos. Prepared breakfast for everyone. Any other furniture and Quarters equipment would already have been installed from local Naval sources - hopefully!

The waiting time before the train moved off seemed endless. I sat tense and praying fervently that no V2 would explode in our particular area before THE GETAWAY!

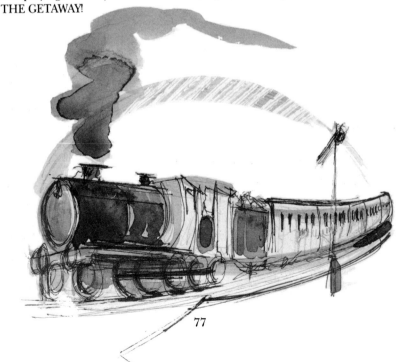

At last! The laboured and somewhat jerky movement of the train heralded that historic departure. Excited talk for a while. The London Wrens not liking this move from home; those from over the Border, jubilant with anticipation. But all were equally exhausted after the past hectic days of preparation. Silence fell...

Suddenly, I was wide awake. The train had stopped in what looked like the middle of nowhere. Railway staff and naval Officers were hurrying down the corridor of the train. I got to my feet and chased after them staying the last man in his tracks. I learned that 'only a couple of coaches had become detached. No personnel involved. Just the pianos and the mess tables. They would have to stay in a siding and come the next day.'

So the 'picnic breakfast' became just that, with Wrens sitting in wide circles on the floors of their respective dining rooms. In The Hydro we used the ballroom!

Each of my two Third Officers is now in charge of the outlying Quarters, Strathclyde, by the river and Birkenward at the top of the village. Craigevar is close to The Hydro and shares the same messing.

So James, this is the picture, so far.

From a brief preliminary glance, I realise that the basic cleaning has taken place and an enormous supply of COCKROACH ELIMINATOR is stacked in one of those pantries alongside the main galley here.

May the Operation be both *rapid* and *successful.*

Spare us a thought...!

Anna

HMS COPRA
Skelmorlie Hydro
Wemyss Bay
Renfrewshire

Dear James

Please forgive the lack of communication since our arrival here in Skelmorlie. I cannot say that I have not had the time to write. One can always make the time. I can only put it down to adjustment.

Life here is so completely alien from that we left behind us in Chelsea a few short weeks ago, but already seeming worlds away.

For instance, now being able at any time to step out into the open without tin hat and gas mask and, for me, notebook and pencil in hand.

To sleep, or try to sleep, in a normal bed and drop the habit of listening,

listening for that distant wasp-like buzzing coming nearer, clearer every second. Tensing up for the inevitable explosion and hopefully escaping a near one. I am told this adjusting process can take a matter of weeks.

Meantime, up here we are receiving welcome help in many ways from our neighbouring Base along the road. The Admiral himself springing an occasional surprise visit and always getting his salute in first!

Several beautifully packaged American Nissen huts now await erection in a large hedge-screened area, formerly the Hydro's kitchen garden. From this fact, I can only conclude that our numbers are due for expansion. But one of the huts is immediately earmarked for a Chapel.

We are in Scotland. Sunday transport is cut to a minimum. There are various and different denominations in our own personnel. Therefore a central and universal place of worship is imperative.

So the moment the structure was assembled, we had volunteers in plenty for decorating and cleaning of the interior. One of these was our new young Naval Chaplain, currently on long leave. I have a feeling he is a survivor from some incident we are never likely to hear about.

The decorating proved a much longer task than we had anticipated. We had failed to realise that an arched ceiling is a vastly greater area than a flat surface. This particular one swallowed up gallons of paint and almost our last ounce of energy. Dusk was upon us as we finally locked the door on our labours.

Back in the Hydro we presented our Chaplain with a large tablet of soap, an outsize bath towel and the loan of the Guest bathroom. Then invited him to dinner.

On Monday evenings, he holds a Confirmation class in the only available and quiet room in this whole establishment, namely a Guest bedroom (cabin) at the far end of a corridor in our Officers' Wing.

The Officer detailed to organise the preparation of this room for the initial Class came to me and asked if I thought this venue was quite proper for the occasion.

'Absolutely,' I assured her. 'There is nowhere else. And above all, don't you breathe a word of these scruples to anyone concerned, or you will never ever be allowed to live it down.'

But back to our newly erected Chapel across the road. It serves all denominations in this Wren community, therefore we require a Service rota.

The respective Priests and Ministers are already devoted to their civilian flock on Sundays, therefore our services are spread across the week. Whoever officiates comes into the wardroom for breakfast with me after the Service.

On Wednesday it is our Padré. On Friday a young Roman Catholic Priest. This latter is a Bing Crosby fan. If I am not present when he arrives, I am quickly made aware of *his* presence by the strains of the latest Crosby hit on our wireless. I am told the young man is very social and goes skating with the Wren officers based a few miles up river.

To return again to our Chapel - we have received generous gifts or loans for the furnishing and general embellishment of the interior. These include a small harmonium. One or two of the Wrens can offer their services as organist and our Chaplain is a gifted musician and one-time chorister of Kings College, Cambridge. As you can imagine, his splendid voice leads the singing.

Greenery from the hedgerows and gifts of flowers from friends and neighbours beautified and enriched our opening Service which was (and continues to be always) open to visitors.

In a matter of a few weeks all the huts were assembled and occupied. There just remained the weather-proofing. A truck load of sailors arrived and started the painting of the exteriors with tar, melted on the site over an open fire; the container suspended from a tripod, keeping liquid tar warm above the flame. Come eleven o'clock, one and all downed brushes and hurried off towards the Hydro galley for refreshment. I took this opportunity to walk up to the site and see what progress had been made and, rounding a corner was horrified to see boiling tar spilling over and, now a molten flame, creeping towards the hut.

Fire hydrants were quite near, mercifully, but by the time the alarm was given, and these were put into use, there was a considerable blaze. Switchboard had alerted Naval and Town Fire Brigades.

A Wren came flying towards me. Her jacket was on a chair at the far end of that hut and in the pocket was a letter just received from her husband. It was unopened. He was away at sea. She had had no news for weeks and she was desperate to have that letter. The outside of the hut was well ablaze at that end. I could see the jacket. It looked small and, to me, just a jacket. To her at that moment it was EVERYTHING. I pushed her inside. 'Run, snatch the jacket and run, run.' I kept on repeating it. 'Run! Run!' it seemed to be the only word in the world at that moment.

She made a grab at the jacket, held it tightly and RAN...

That one hut had to be replaced, but our Chapel escaped any damage. Write soon James...

Anna

Dear James

Well you may find this difficult to believe, but just three weeks after the recorded incident in my last letter, I was awakened in the middle of the night by a Duty Wren bearing the alarming news that the Stores were on fire.

Out of sheer habit I was into slacks and tunic and tin hat in a matter of seconds. It turned out, in fact, to be the *stokehold* which was on fire. And really well ablaze.

Mercifully, this building was detached from the main Hydro though but a narrow strip of grass and pathway lay between them. Up a short stone stairway, on the Hydro side of the stokehold was a small Drystore, housing surplus (unopened) foodstuffs, and cleaning requisites.

My Supply Staff, clasping the keys to this store, were all agog to start a salvage operation. So, we formed a long chain well away from the blaze and, hopefully, the tainting smoke and they dumped cases and packages beneath trees and bushes ready for removal when daylight arrived.

The Stokers, oblivious of this drama were sleeping in their hut beyond the vegetable garden and had to be alerted.

Meantime, I held a conference with the Sick Bay Staff. Their premises lay directly adjacent to that piece of ground whereon the fire was now raging.

Unless a North-east wind suddenly arose (which seemed unlikely) or the Fire Service were delayed, the main Hydro should escape damage. However, the fumes would penetrate into all that end of the building, leaving the sick even sicker.

And the damping down and general aftermath would continue for several hours. So in complete *silence*, we moved and established Sick Bay in a quiet warm location at the further end of the Hydro.

Duty PO asked 'Should we ring the fire bell?' The very idea horrified me! She got a very firm 'No!' for an answer. The picture of a couple of hundred Wrens in various night attire milling around the grounds and garden space in semi or complete darkness...this, plus a couple of dozen sailors with orders to 'look out for danger and deal with it immediately'.

Well James, the fire was extinguished, Service departed, leaving a truck load of sailors to patrol the area in case of any stray sparks.

I decided that it was not worth my while to go to bed. I would see how the *Patrol* was faring. I searched around but drew a blank. So I targeted the Naval Transport in which they had come. Well, believe it or not, there they were and every Jack Tar fast asleep!

I was the sole 'Firewatcher'. But not for long!

Next day of course, everyone of rank or merit from the Admiral down, was on our doorstep. Everything was put in motion. Emergency heating was installed. Civil Engineers from Greenoch tramped around, filling their notebooks and asking questions. But that was not the end of it.

Chief Officer WRNS... *our* Chief Officer, informed me that I was to receive the *Captain's Commendation* before the whole Ship's Company. Not only Wrens but Naval Officers, Petty Officers and Ratings.

I went at once and told Chief Officer that I could not possibly go through with this ordeal. Certainly not on my own. For it entailed standing up alone on one side of the square and facing (ranged on the other three sides) the WHOLE of Ship's Company, Officers, Petty Officers and Ratings. I never ascertained where the Captain would stand but from some prominent and wholly audible stance THE COMMENDATION would be delivered.

I pleaded that this fire had absolutely *nothing* to do with any of the Wrens, it was entirely the fault of the duty Stoker, who had damped down too quickly and who, moreover, had left a wooden chair and spread-out newspaper within range of a backfire flame. The perfect recipe for what indeed followed.

So came The Day.

Myself, and all the Petty Officers and Duty Wrens who had been on duty that particular night, stood along one side of the Hollow Square and all the rest crowded up on the other three sides.

The Captain made his Commendation.

Nursing Sister said she had never seen me look so poker-faced!

Well James, following on this, FIRE was uppermost in the mind of everyone. I think I mentioned the high tower at one corner of the Hydro. A fire escape has now been fitted to that tiny lookout window. It is a small armchair on pulleys. From the lawn below it looks about big enough to hold a doll! The day arrived when this contraption was to be tested. Volunteers were called for.

Naturally, as Quarters Officer, it was my duty to follow the Fire Officer. He was coming from Naval Headquarters. My two Assistant Officers put their names forward, followed by Chief, Petty Officers and one or two Leading Wrens.

We invited the Fire Officer to lunch and then the Demonstrators toiled up the spiral staircase and crowded into the little room beside that window.

It was my turn after the Fire Officer. The worst part was getting out of the small window and into the chair. Whatever happened one must not, MUST NOT look down. The LETTING GO was the crucial moment. Getting into the chair and seated and the safety bar across the chest was tricky but there were still hands within reach. The propelling oneself into space was the crux. After that it was a matter of pushing away from the wall during the descent, trying to keep facing squarely up to those red bricks and not getting into any sort of spin or wobble.

Our audience, forming what looked from above like a square of navy serge sprinkled with pale blobs, these were the uniforms and the upturned faces of the Ship's Company. As each of us demonstrators stepped out safely from that small chair, a cheer went up for us.

Last week, coming up from the local bus stop by the shore, I discovered a box containing 56 pounds of CURRANTS sitting there in isolation since the night of the fire!

Glancing casually across this peaceful estuary, one would think that nothing much ever happened here!

Anna

HMS COPRA
Skelmorlie Hydro
November 1944

Dear James

Third Officer March wrote saying that at last the chance had arisen for her to accept the long-standing invitation to visit us.

All arrangements were made. However before the arrival date, I had chanced to meet with the Admiral's wife (Grousie, you may remember) who told me that there was to be a dance at the Hotel in Largs. She was arranging to give a dinner party. She was sending me an invitation. I explained about Third Officer March but was assured that she also would be invited.

So, the evening promised to be our highlight. It proved to be just that. A splendid dinner in a relaxed and happy atmosphere. We danced to a superb Royal Marines Band (the RM are the most musical of any of the services) and the whole evening was delightful.

Next day, over lunch at Skelmorlie, Nursing Sister suddenly remarked,

'Second Officer, you were gloorious last night, so you were. Never did you have a dancing partner with less than fourr rrings arroont his arrm.'

'Sister,' I replied, 'Twas the wine was doing the counting for you.'

But she could have been right. It was a terrific dance. All too soon, I was seeing 3/O March onto her train for London. But we had managed a few short walks and had caught up on a huge backlog of news and gossip. A day or two after this I met a Naval Commander who had been a guest at the dinner. Who was my friend? He had found her quite delightful. I must not forget to pass on this piece of information.

Here, our latest innovation is Sunday Afternoon Tea Dances. The swimming pool also is available to guests. This is becoming increasingly popular since there is little else on offer and no public transport.

Hallowe'en provided another occasion for dancing; but preceded by a sort of preliminary ritual in the houses.

The dance was held in the Hydro. Small children from the village, swathed in white sheets, their faces unrecognizable under weird masks of self-inflicted make-up, suddenly and rather alarmingly appeared amongst the dancers. I wondered if their parents knew! Just one thing worried me. Supposing one of these young sprites were to go exploring this vast building and consequently be locked in for the night.

I doubled the Duty Watch, expressing my fears.

Mercifully we had no stowaways.

Our local electrician and shop owner, said there was to be a Supper and Barn Dance at a farm some four miles inland. This in aid of the Red Cross. He would be delighted to provide transport in his car for any two or three Wren Officers who might wish to go. Driven by curiosity about Scottish farm life, I accepted this first hand opportunity and with two others, risked the journey through snow-bound country under a brilliant full moon and hardening frost.

The farmhouse stood out large, square and solid; its heavy outer door, half-shut for protection, half open in welcome.

The evening started with supper. The ritual, I found fascinating. Hosts and hostess entertained their family and many relations in an upstairs drawing room. This room remaining closed to all others.

Guests considered to be of some merit, high standing or a cut above the rest (this included us!) were allotted the dining room. Now this room personified solidity.

A massive centre table, spread with damask, starched and dazzling white but scarcely visible beneath the wealth of home-baked delicacies spread thereon.

An equally solid sideboard supported an amazing number of silver trophies and cups of varying sizes, all bearing inscriptions, which distance prevented my reading. But it took no time at all to deduce that the winners of these many awards, prize highland Bulls, were portrayed in oils, framed in gilt and displayed upon the four walls around this room.

At a given signal, we rose and made our way towards the barn, (remember, this was a BARN dance). En route, we passed the large kitchen where supped smallholders, villagers and a motley of outlying cottagers. The scullery was reserved for farmhands and casual labour (I wondered who drew the dividing lines!).

Mercifully, we could reach the dance through covered and protected precincts. The barn itself was a huge building, the interior wall a dazzle of whitewash, the floor spotless and inviting. There were deep alcoves in the walls. These held trays of sprouting potatoes. I wondered about this and I had the idea that I might ask but glancing around, the glorious tartan of the different clans portrayed in those kilts, the dark velvet of the jackets, the lace of the cravats. Somehow, these seemed to have little affinity with seed potatoes, (in Yorkshire we call them 'Sets').

The band was tuning up, every foot was tapping and then they were off! I say *they* because I retreated into a shadow. Knowing absolutely nothing of the intricacies of the various steps, I deemed it wiser to be an onlooker. The kilted giants in those buckled shoes, moving light as any fairy. It all appeared effortless, despite the whirling pace.

I ventured to find a seat in the shadows but a moment later and without any preliminary request, found myself part of the bewildering whirl.

At the end of this, it was no surprise that my partner suggested a visit to the bar. Now the bar was a converted dairy, white and spotless and of below zero temperature. Without consultation, a glass of neat Scotch was thrust into my hand. I doubt if there was an alternative! However, our little party did realise what we were imbibing and there were no incidents.

It had snowed afresh whilst we danced.

We started home, the moon high, the landscape untouched, was simply breathtaking. For that brief journey alone, the whole excursion had been worthwhile.

Write soon if you have a spare moment.

Anna

Dear James

The confirmation classes ended last week and our Guest Cabin is now restored to its rightful use. Chaplain called to inform me that the Service of Confirmation is to be held in the Private Chapel of the Bishop of Glasgow. Would I represent the parents and Godparents of our Wren Candidates?

Surely I would. So arrangements were put in hand.

Come the appointed day, we had an early lunch and our Chaplain collected us. He had borrowed a small brake from the Naval dockyard up river. I sat beside the driver and was regaled with tales of his boyhood in Northern Ireland.

Without hitch or hesitation, we arrived at our destination. My impression of the Chapel was that of a rather narrow oblong structure, the ceiling so far above as to be scarcely visible in the dim lighting of prevailing wartime restrictions.

A deep, rich crimson carpeting over the tiled floor created a softening, warm effect on the sombre carvings and furnishings.

The rest of the candidates filed into the Chapel. These were seven men, currently patients from a nearby Services Hospital. All were independently mobile.

We, the members of the congregation, numbered not more than half a dozen. After the Service, we were given tea in a small library in the Palace, where largely thanks to our Chaplain, everyone circulated and chatted in a happy and relaxed atmosphere.

Driving home through the black-out demanded all the attention of our man at the wheel. Passengers seemed to be falling asleep. There was silence. We deposited the Wrens at their various Quarters and Chaplain stayed to dinner. He left almost immediately afterwards. He wished, he said, to write to the parents of his Candidates on this day of their Confirmation.

Anna

Dear James

Happy New Year!

Thank you, thank you for the lovely Christmas and New Year parcels. I fear my offering was but a poor paper-back instead of the volume intended, but in the end I had to forego my trip to Glasgow and content myself with whatever these local shops had to offer.

Here, as you can imagine, we had non-stop celebrations. In duplicate; first for Christmas and second for Hogmanay. I called a General Meeting - All Welcome.

We discussed, voted and agreed on events covering the seven days of Christmas followed by the seven days of New Year.

Villagers were to be invited, plus friends from the accessible neighbourhood. There were to be Whist Drives for the more mature, followed by refreshments and perhaps a little gentle (!) dancing.

For the rest, Treasure Hunts during daylight, Table Tennis Tournaments, Competitive Swimming, Copra men included in all events. A celebration dance for Boxing night, likewise on New Year's Eve (Hogmanay). These with full dance orchestra.

Two of our Wren Artists promised poster programmes to be displayed in the Ballroom. Cooks promised refreshment for every occasion.

Our Chaplain organised a Christmas morning Service to be held in the largest area, that is, the ballroom. It was to be the Nine Lessons and Carols Service. He asked me if I would read one of the lessons and which would I choose? Without hesitation, I chose the one beginning 'And there were Shepherds watching their flocks'. I would be at home there.

Chaplain sang a solo carol. It was lovely to hear, I think I told you he was a King's Scholar at Cambridge in his youth. Everyone came to the Service.

We had a splendid

dance on Boxing Day evening and of course Hogmanay was THE event. I do not know where so many braw young Scotsmen came from but their dress and their prowess in dancing left me (for one) in a daze of admiration.

At the end of the dancing (about 2am) one of our Petty Officers came to me and asked if she and the other Wren PO's could go 'First Footing'. She promised they would be back for breakfast! I said 'Yes', of course. It would be the experience of a lifetime for most of them.

The weather was kind. We managed every event on the programme.

Anna

HMS COPRA
Skelimore Hydro
Largs
March 1945

Dear James

After the Christmas celebrations ended, we three Officers needed a short respite. So, off went the first of us and during her Leave, her promotion came through. Added to this she returned with an engagement ring on her finger!

Unhappily, I had caught a streaming cold and Sister banished me to my cabin and my bed.

For some obscure reason, our Chaplain called and was invited to stay to dinner and celebrate the double occasion. I had no idea that the dividing wall between my cabin and our wardroom was so flimsy! There were but four persons round that dining table; but the uproar - occasioned by the celebration of the two rings, one on her arm and one on her finger - had to be heard to be believed! And I was sure it was not water they were drinking. My supposition was confirmed when Sister came into my cabin bearing a modest glass of something which was *not* a doctor's prescription.

Thus within a few days we had said our farewells and voiced our blessings and were welcoming a new member to our small wardroom.

She is a Scot, so should feel not too strange up here and indeed may provide a useful interpreter when sometimes a local expression stumps me completely. If she proves to be suitably tough, I could put her in charge of local labour! Though I doubt if it would ever come to that, since Base and Dockyard are practically on our doorstep. Normally, they are available for repairs and emergencies...

From a visiting ship in Greenoch, we received an invitation to take a trip up river and to have lunch on board. They could accommodate three Officers and twenty Wrens.

We embarked at a small jetty quite close to our Quarters on a fine, calm morning. Small groups were in turn shown around. The Operations room was particularly interesting, especially the radar screen showing what was going on in the depths of the river bed. Fascinating to watch a large fish swimming gracefully across our view. We glimpsed into the galley where our lunch was being prepared.

Drinks, followed by luncheon and then we were put off somewhere well up river where transport had been arranged to take us back to Skelmorlie.

Several days after this excursion one of our Wren Officers and myself were on a duty visit to the Base and had a chance meeting with two of our hosts from the river trip. Over a sherry, we learned to our amazement, that whilst our visit was in full swing on that vessel, the magic underwater detector had in fact detected an enemy submarine away up river. Of all the tricky situations they had ever encountered, this, they thought, must be the worst! But the Silent Service remained silent.

Throughout that pleasant and leisurely luncheon, we had absolutely no idea that the Operations Room was drawing up emergency plans for the evacuation of their Wren guests.

Mercifully, this situation did not arise, or I might not be writing this letter to you today!

Anna

HMS COPRA
Skelmorlie Hydro
April 1945

Dear James

We three Wren Officers at Skelmorlie have acquired a Champion; or should I say Fairy Godmother. In reality, she is a local resident who was invited to our Christmas activities, which events seem to have created a lasting impression. This is scarcely surprising since absolutely nothing on such a scale seems ever to have happened in this area; even in pre-war days.

As I recall, this guest took to the floor only twice during the evening in question and each time for a waltz, slow and stately. But certainly, in her gown of dark, rich silk, a matching velvet ribbon through her silver hair, exquisite jewels at wrist and throat, indeed the whole effect was highly romantic. I learn that Miss MacRae (for that is her name), lives in a large bungalow on the edge of this village, where she keeps a full staff of elderly retainers, from butler to kitchen maid. Her chauffeur fell outside this happy age group and is currently helping to win the war.

Though Miss MacRae offered her services to the Voluntary Drivers Club, there seems to be little demand. She therefore has turned her patriotic and eager intentions in our direction. We are for the moment her War Effort. For, in her opinion, we three are sadly overworked. The best tonic in such a situation, could be a day in Glasgow. My two Third Officers chose their separate dates. Both, it would seem, returned speechless from fatigue but just managing to phone and excuse themselves from putting in an appearance. They would tell me all about it tomorrow.

Therefore, in some measure, I was prepared for an exhausting shop-gazing tour when my date came up. But it turned out to be not quite like that. Taxi to a local station, train to Glasgow and our day began.

First, a coffee, then detailed exploration of one of the large department stores. Did I wish to make a purchase? Well, it is so long since I had entered shops such as these, I just could not think of anything that I either needed or fancied.

We would take a short cut to our luncheon venue where our table had been reserved. And James, it was here that we met our fate.

In a Fishmonger's window was displayed a whole large Haddock. Silver, gleaming, fresh as a daisy!

With a cry of triumph, Miss MacRae darted into that shop.

'Oh what a *thrill* for cook. She has had me on the lookout for exactly this, these three months past.'

We left the shop with our purchase wrapped...but *only just*. Paper is *scarce* and what we must not forget, is *rationed*.

This fishmonger is striving to be a true patriot and at the same time, keep a hold on a valued customer.

I felt he aimed to strike a just balance. In reality, falling far short of our minimum requirements. Clutching her prize and with a happy smile, my hostess asked, 'Now, which route shall we take to luncheon?' I suggested the shortest.

So we lunched in the restaurant of a large department store, Prize Purchase lying at our feet.

From thence but a step to the Theatre in time for the Matinée.

The short cup-of-tea interval posed our first problem. We decided to divide the limited time evenly. Thus, No 1 for the tea break whilst No 2 kept Haddock watch. Then a smart change over. It worked.

Our next goal was Miss MacRae's Club, where we were to dine. Should we take a taxi? I thought a breath of fresh air might be beneficial after the theatre.

There was a short-cut through side alleys and among these we stumbled upon my real objective, a Newsagents and general corner shop, since it was becoming more apparent with every step that our treasure was in dire need of further covering. Faint damp patches were already appearing through that inadequate wrapping paper.

Voicing my intentions to Miss MacRae, I dived into the shop. But all was not so straightforward as anticipated. Newspapers only to order. Did I not know that paper was in short supply?

I did, from experience, fully realise the truth of these words. But at this moment, I had an emergency. Two large sheets of almost anything would be preferable to nothing.

I fingered a half-crown thoughtfully, silently, openly. It worked. I came out of the shop in triumph. Though I must say that by this time our burden was beginning to take on a somewhat suspect appearance. But it was perfectly obvious that my hostess was a member of considerable importance in that prestigious club. For our package was received with as much grace as if it were a bunch of roses. Safe from all ills (hopefully) it was placed on a ledge, owner's personal card beside it.

So, to the meal. Instinctively, but without comment, we both chose a green salad in preference to the fish course. The meal was leisurely and quite delicious.

We left for the train with our burden intact and Miss MacRae, being tall, was able to place it upon the luggage rack and even more mercifully, directly above herself.

A few minutes before ETA, I dared to look upwards. Our problem did show a faint damp patch on its underside. I simply had not the courage to let my anxious gaze stray to the crown of that exquisite toque of sealskin which lay in direct line below.

Our taxi driver was on the platform. 'Anything for me to carry, Miss MacRae, ma'am?' There was.

They halted the taxi to put me down at the Hydro. Showering my thanks on my hostess, I assured her she had given me a simply unforgettable day.

No truer word spoken.

Anna

Dear James

Margot has left us. Her draft came through last week. She worked at the Base, so I did not see a great deal of her. But since we experienced the awful trauma of the Guards Chapel together, we have become good friends.

The new Admin Assistant is young, attractive, newly married and missing her husband, currently overseas. Janice is her name. By chance, Janice and I met up on Sunday morning, whilst I was awaiting my after Church bus, (I manage the 8am Service in Largs and breakfast as guest of the dear Canon at the Rectory. He leaves immediately for his next Service and I await the one and only Sunday transport to Skelmorlie).

Janice and I were passing a flight of steps leading up to a large hotel. Janice asked what the hotel was like. I could not say, since I had never been anywhere in this town except in those establishments currently belonging to the Royal Navy.

Had I time to join her for a coffee? Just time, I reckoned. So we mounted the steps and entered a spacious, many-windowed lounge, apparently deserted. But not wholly, for on a far off window seat two Naval Lieutenants were having drinks.

They came over and asked if they might join us. They had put into Greenoch for a minor repair to their vessel and were awaiting sailing orders.

Would we go on board and dine with them on the morrow? We were delighted to accept this invitation and would be at the jetty by 6pm. Since they were currently awaiting a 'phone call one stayed at the hotel whilst the other accompanied us to the bus stop. 'See you tomorrow' were his parting words.

So next evening found Janice and me at the appointed hour being met by a small motor launch manned by a Petty Officer and Leading Seaman.

It took less than ten minutes to reach our destination, a yacht in sombre wartime camouflage, anchored in the lee of a tiny island. Our hosts were awaiting us and we stayed on deck for drinks. Blackout regulations forced us below where dinner was waiting.

They had made great efforts over the meal, and we sent congratulations to their cook.

About halfway through the first course, a note was delivered to our senior host. He slipped it into his pocket without comment. The unspoken message in a quick glance exchanged across the table, did not escape my notice.

Could this be immediate sailing orders? If so, I would be absolutely intrigued to know what they might do with Janice and me. Would we have to swim for the shore?!

No word spoken. The meal proceeded.

Our hosts had a very fine gramophone and good classical records. We all chose in turn our favourite items.

Departure time came all too soon. In company with the two officers we made the brief trip back to the jetty from whence I had organised return transport with a Skelmorlie neighbour in her car.

The car was waiting. We expressed our warmest thanks, said goodbye and I dropped Janice at Wren Quarters and then continued to Skelmorlie. Duty Watch had nothing to report. I duly signed the book. Sleep came quickly, but not for long!

Someone was shaking me. There was a *noise*...NOISE everywhere and the Duty Wren still shaking me, her voice urgent ...happy, excited. No alarm, a different tone of urgency. 'Ma'am, the war is over, the WAR IS OVER! May we get up. The war is over - OVER!'

In no time I was in muffler, slacks and jacket. From force of habit I picked up the tin hat - then threw it down. It was redundant now. Ships hooting in the river...ships hooting, bells ringing. A huge cacophony of sound, invading every tiny pocket of silence.

'May we get up?'

'Of course.'

They streamed down from every cabin, hugging one another, thrusting feet into slippers, arms into dressing gowns. Two pianists clambered onto the stage and gave the piano the trouncing of a lifetime.

There was singing and dancing non-stop.

Tragically here and there a tearful mourner was being comforted by close friends, then stoically joining up with them in the whirl of celebration.

For two hours we sang and danced. Then Duty Chief came to me and said they were exhausted and could they go to bed. Pianist struck up the National Anthem and within ten minutes every light was out. Silence took over. Duty Watch gave one final walk-about. Nursing Sister calmed her little brood and checked one or two temperatures, dimmed all lights...

There was movement outside. Banging on doors and windows and a male chorus...'We want the Wrens, the Wrens. We want the Wrens.'

I strode to the entrance and found myself confronted by a whole party of men Petty Officers at the ready for a riotous all-night orgy.

Or so they thought.

I faced them. 'Not at this hour! They have already been celebrating for the past two hours, are completely exhausted and requested an end to the party. You can collect the Wrens after breakfast tomorrow until midnight.'

"The Wrens at Greenoch are out with the men. We want the Wrens.'

'Well, you are just too late,' I looked at my watch. 'Tomorrow is not so far away.'

The disgruntled revellers sloped off. All had been drinking. I instructed a Duty Wren to take a circuitous route to the huts across the road and contact every PO in charge. All doors and windows were to be firmly locked. Every light to be extinguished.

So, come next morning, from all Wren Quarters like flocks of starlings making for fields of newly cleared stubble, they scattered away and out of sight or sound.

That is, all except one.

A young Third Officer appeared. Could she spend the day with me? She did not feel like junketing. I knew her brother had been a casualty. Her thoughts were with her parents.

We put up sandwiches and thermos flasks and went out into the hills, taking narrow paths between rocks and heather. From a vantage point, we looked far down to the blue, almost silent waters of the estuary, where the land stopped and gave way to the dominant ocean. For today was different. No angry, slapping, bullying waves hurling themselves against the rocks.

Instead, an almost subservient incoming tide, murmuring, reticent, almost requesting permission to enter.

No spray spitting, no crashing or walloping, just a courtesy visit and quiet retreat.

It was Peace Day.

Write soon, please.

Anna

Dear James

Now that the junketing is over, we must turn the page and start an entirely new chapter. I do not quite know what would be a suitable heading...'Into Peace' could be safely unpredictable!

As elsewhere throughout the country, our initial step here in Largs was a Service of Thanksgiving, attended by all religious denominations, all Fighting Services, the Scouts, Guides, Cubs, Brownies, the Voluntary Services and many more. From far and near, the aged and infirm, some in invalid chairs; the very young, in mothers' arms or prams or pushchairs, they came.

Priests, Vicars, Pastors and Lay-Preachers played their part in the leading of this great and glorious thanksgiving for peace.

So far, there has not been so much as a whisper of Copra's return to London. Indeed, can we be certain that the Chelsea we left behind us will still be there intact and untouched by the V2s?

But back to Skelmorlie...we can now travel safely over water. This means a considerable widening of recreational activities. The ending of blackout restrictions adds to the general sense of this new-found freedom.

There are Wrens across the water and a Royal Marine establishment with RM Wrens further down this coast. So, with Gouroch and Greenoch, there should be no lack of competition.

Apart from the signature of Approval by an Officer, the whole Sports Committee is in the hands of the Ships Company of HMS Copra. Matches and return matches should carry them through the summer months.

We three Wren Officers are overdue for leave. My turn came last but was delayed by a totally unexpected change of Administration Officer.

In the end, we were just into September when I got away. Well, part of the way...

My 'through' train came to a halt on Newcastle Station. I was assured that I could get a good train at 7am the next morning. By this time it was 10pm so I sought the ladies waiting room. A wide-open door revealed a cold, dark cavern. I entered and made towards a narrow Information window in the farthest corner. This revealed a well-lighted room with a roaring fire and an unfriendly attendant.

Her room was Private. My predicament had nothing to do with her. The Public Waiting Room wherein I stood would be open all night. No, I could NOT close the door. It was securely fixed in its present position.

In semi-darkness, I stretched out on the cold, horsehair sofa and spread my greatcoat over me.

There were voices, male voices. Someone was shining a torch on my face. Two Policeman were bending over me. I raised my head to show that I was not a corpse. Question and answer...question and answer...

One of the two Policemen went to the lighted window of that inner sanctum and within minutes I was ^esconced therein.

And none too soon, for about twenty minutes later, there was a commotion. A singing, shouting, staggering drunk lurched from the platform, through the conveniently wide-open doorway, and beyond that into distant quarters. He continued the racket so was easily traced and doubtless put under lock and key for the remainder of the night. Bless those two lovely Policemen! Thus passed the remainder of that night in fitful dozing, waking, sleeping.

Six-thirty. Tea was being brewed in the adjoining kitchenette. My train left at 7am. There seemed to be no spare tea.

I went out onto the platform and became an ordinary passenger.

Arriving eventually at Ripon, fortune changed. A taxi driver had just deposited his fare and yes, he could get me home.

I ventured only to the edge of the now barren woods... It had been a long hard winter with rain and snow. Timber wagons had cut deep into the rain sodden earth, crushing the life out of erstwhile spring flowers. The snowdrops, primroses, anemones, marsh marigolds, would never again see the light of day.

Everywhere there was silence. It was forlorn, battered, wide-open. No nesting places, no bird song. But there were rabbits. Taking over, establishing themselves, threatening everything edible within reach.

Now that there were no trees filtering the light and creating a green shadowy wonderland, the magic was gone out of the place. I would not go back until it was replanted and living again.

Time was spent visiting friends and relations, meeting new babies! Riding whenever and wherever possible.

Then came a sort of bombshell...

A telegram delivered into my hand as I rounded a corner of the garden. It read 'To FIRST OFFICER etc etc - congratulations on your promotion and appointment to WRNS Training, Mill Hill. Your relief reporting a.m. 17th. Suggest you stay on leave until September 15th, Signed, etc.'

This was followed by a second telegram...

'Congratulations on your well-earned promotion. Admiral Horan.'

Surely one of the highlights of my whole life! The added Leave time enabled me to get my uniforms cleaned and the half ring stitched into place! And best of all, I am spending a weekend with 3/O March on my way back to London. So, now to the final handing over to my successor.

The Christian fellowship Group invited me to their current weekly gathering and presented me with a Book of Prayers. I was quite overcome and felt honoured. They had always been in charge of their own weekly meetings under the experienced guidance of my PO Supply.

Next morning, I went down to the Base to say goodbye to the Admiral and Grousie and Doodles and everyone. My favourite Captain asked me to have a drink with him.

Thus the final departure, allowing time for the promised weekend with 3/O March.

Not wishing for a repetition of that frightful night on Newcastle Station, I decided on an overnight stop in Glasgow and booked in at a well-run Officers' Club. My two Third Officers decided to come with me for that final night; even though it meant breakfasting at 6am, on the following morning. Back to Skelmorlie for them; hopefully straight through to Kings Cross for me.

Later…

The happy weekend over - 3/O March in great form - I proceeded to Mill Hill, knowing only that this new establishment accommodates ONE THOUSAND Wren personnel.

Now my new OIC is no stranger, for it was she who recommended me for a Commission in those far off days at Englands Lane. Here, I get a slight feeling of trepidation on her part. Could I be one of her pigeons coming home to roost?

My new address:
First Officer etc
WRNS Training Establishment
Mill Hill
LONDON

Write soon.

Anna

Dear James

Do you realise that this is my eleventh address since I joined the Service? Well, the twelfth if you count that strange switch-over at Plymouth. And unless anything untoward and inexplicable should occur, this will be the final appointment of my Service career.

As you may remember, I had arranged a happy interim weekend with Third Officer March. She is now Quarters Officer away in the countryside in Buckinghamshire, her home county, which is fortunate for her. By cycling on duty to near exhaustion point thus reserving her petrol, she had managed to accumulate the required amount to get us to her home for the weekend.

The weather was perfect. We walked and talked, and talked and walked, and made outline plans for our next meeting, now that we are within visiting distance.

Third Officer March saw me onto my London train and thrust a bunch of exquisite roses from her garden into my hand. Well James, in the mad rush of arrival in London, I left my roses on the luggage rack. I felt bereft. It seemed a miserable and somehow disadvantaged start into the unknown. I kept seeing that bit of luggage rack and the gradually wilting flowers (really this was quite ridiculous, someone was sure to rescue the roses).

My CO here and now was the OIC at Englands Lane who recommended me for a Commission. She had not set eyes on me since I left Englands Lane for O.T.C. and the wearing of the white armband.

This whole building is something like a cement fortress from the outside. From the interior, a non-stop human machine. During the very long working day, I doubt whether one could find a quiet corner anywhere.

Despite the vast proportions of this edifice, I cannot understand why, out of all the rooms available, someone never thought of locating the most quiet and remote room and dedicating it for use as a Chapel.

But back to the building itself, which is very high with a flat circular roof, open to the sky and reached by a flight of stone steps. I am not sure how many steps but by the time one reaches the open air from ground level, well, surely it could not be less than one thousand! Window frames are steel, doors pseudo-wood. Everything fireproof, I guess. It is geared to hold one thousand personnel but it is in the process of closing down and has reached a complement of eight hundred to date.

The premises are the property of the Medical Research Council, who, now that it is safe to do so, are anxious to re-establish themselves. We had a top-level meeting here with some MPs and two or three high-ups in the medical world. We gave them coffee and agreed on a handover date of April 2nd. Training continues but with a decreasing number each week. By the end of March, intake will cease and we shall start closing down and finally handing over to the medics. Then the Wrens Training will be transferred gradually to a camp site at Reading in Berkshire.

But a number will still be here over Christmas and the cooks are preparing for that. As is the custom, one of our prestigious Naval officers attended the Christmas pudding stirring ceremony. He sloshed *pints* of rum into the mixture!

Meantime, I try to find my way around. After the remoteness and peace of Skelmorlie, the dizzy whirl of this establishment comes as something of a shock. Doubtless I shall find myself a part of it in no time at all. I am detailed to deliver two lectures per week to the new entries.

The medics have a field adjoining this building with a bungalow type construction at the far end, too far away for an accurate description. White-coated figures are to be seen down there and occasionally they appear up here and invade the cellars. Now these cellars are their property but they also come under our jurisdiction for Fire Watch.

A list outside the Wardroom door informs me that I am Fire Watch Officer next week and also gives me the name of my team. A nice helpful junior Officer paused beside me as I studied the list. She cleared her throat, hesitated, cleared her throat again and said, 'Ma'am, I see that you have Wren Simpson on

your fire-team. I think it is only fair to warn you that you may have some difficulty with her over the cellars area.' 'Really? Is that so?' was my reply and I thanked her.

But forewarned is forearmed, and a sensible precautionary measure which I might do well to consider in this case. Accordingly, I hurried through my lunch, obtained the key to the problem area, said nothing to anyone and started my inspection of the cellars.

Well, this was indeed a revelation! These deep archives were the store rooms for a vast number of glass cases or tanks, similar to those housing goldfish or other types of marine life.

But these were not marine and they

were not living. They were, as far as my scant knowledge could assure me, parts of the human body (both outside and inside) preserved in ether, or whatever is used for this purpose.

This sensational perambulation decided me that I and I alone would take over this portion of the Fire Watch; unless any Wren was particularly interested in medicine or planning to be a surgeon. So, we got the issue sorted out and I became quite used to the specimens when my Fire Watch stint came round.

I do not care for my office. It has a blocked-in feeling, being in the midst of a cluster of others of varying sizes. I have an assistant Third Officer but she is slightly disabled and cannot manage the interminable flights of steps and stairs which must be negotiated during a day's work. Actually, I was quite happy to share some added exercise with a rota of volunteers, for our work load cuts out even the faintest hope of any free time this side of Christmas. Climbing and descending steps is quite a good, if somewhat tedious method of keeping fit!

We have an appointed Chaplain who holds one Service on Sunday morning in the main Assembly Hall. It falls to me to read one of the Lessons. This I rehearse in my cabin, hoping to get my voice to carry that required distance. To an onlooker, or indeed listener, who was not in possession of the facts, this exercise might sound like oncoming insanity. There are no onlookers and, so far as I am aware, no listeners. Maybe this locality has numerous places of worship. I shall never know, since once Christmas is past, we shall start on the closing down operation in deadly earnest, and there will be no time to go to a local Church. Doubtless this will change as the numbers diminish.

I plan to see 3/O March for at least one weekend and there are two or three Wren friends from the far-off days who *could* be in London and able to come for a visit and a meal. I mean to seize the opportunity.

Miss Constance Spry, the noted authority on flower arranging, is booked to give us a lecture in the near future. Also a Dutch singer, Jan Van der Goot is booked for a recital. I look forward to both of these events.

You know, James, despite our address and (geographic) proximity to London, I have never taken a bus, a train or even a WALK since my arrival in this place. I must be crazy!

Write soon please...

Anna

100

Dear James

Thank you for the Christmas and New Year mail and all your good wishes. I look forward to reading the book (clever of you to choose my favourite author and the topic of country lore).

It was no surprise to me that Christmas in this Establishment was very different from its predecessors in other Quarters.

Since we are all under one roof, there was no round trip to carve the turkeys. General opinion had it that the highlight of the festival was the singing of carols on the flat roof of the tower here on Christmas Eve.

The long procession assembled at the foot of that daunting flight of stone steps. In the lead, the Nursing Staff in their dark cloaks with scarlet linings; their starched halos dazzling white. The air was completely still as if in honour of the occasion. Everyone's candle stayed alight.

Once on the circular flat roof and allowing for a breath-regaining interval (timed by Nursing Sister) we sang. I wondered if we could be heard from ground level, for, standing up there on that open platform, one felt so much nearer to heaven than to earth! The singing was unquestionably impressive. I reckoned that the idea had attracted most of the best voices in our Establishment.

There was almost complete exodus from here when it came to the seeing in of the New Year. The favourite location being, of course, Trafalgar Square. For some, it would be the chance of a lifetime!

So, now to the somewhat formidable task of closing down this vast establishment and handing it back to the British Medical Council.

We are still entertaining lecturers on a variety of subjects. This with a view to helping the many Wrens leaving the Service and taking up careers in civilian life.

One of these lecturers is Miss Constance Spry, the flower arranging artist and adviser. Came the evening of the lecture, Miss Spry dined with us here, before delivering her talk which was illustrated by colour slides. Standing up there on stage, our speaker looked about similar in height to her tallest gladioli! She is tiny! Her size three shoes had the highest heels as safely possible, whilst on her brown velvet boater, erect and centre front, was positioned the longest cock-pheasant tail feather I have ever seen!

Well, we all enjoyed the lecturer and her enthusiasm and obvious love of everything floral. The very next morning, my office 'phone rang. Miss Constance

Spry to speak with me. First, her thanks for the delicious dinner of the previous evening. Second, now that the war is over, Miss Spry intends to start a Finishing School. Moreover Miss Spry wishes to staff her establishment on the domestic side with 24 Wrens. Will I, therefore, spread the word and kindly let her have names.

Well, I called into my office the Chiefs and the Petty Officers of the domestic categories and gave them a couple of days to 'spread the word'. The unanimous answer - they all wanted to go home and get married!!

So, I tried diplomacy. I 'phoned Miss Spry and said I had circulated the information plus her address. Most of the Wrens needed time before making a decision and some wished to discuss it with their parents. All had been given the address for application. I tendered my heartfelt good wishes for the enterprise.

We had our Dutch singer, Jan van der Goot, one evening. First he came to dinner in our Wardroom. Rumour had it that on a previous visit, there was a caramel dessert after which he had to unseal his jaws before the recital could begin. We arranged what we considered to be a foolproof dessert and this evening passed in tranquil pleasure. But I find it difficult to believe that story! His voice is hauntingly beautiful and stayed with me for days after the event.

Third Officer March came for a short weekend, during which she and I had an altercation re saluting the Quarterdeck (a space near our main entrance). She would not salute SPACE. I told her sternly, that she had enough imagination in her make-up to see Nelson himself in that space if she chose to do so. This was, in truth, one of the worst moments in my whole service career. I was about to be disgraced by my guest. She saluted!

Our OIC has retired, thankful I think, to get back to her home and civilian life. Later, she will be coming to our Closing Down Party. Her successor is filling in here until the final closure and from thence proceeding to an appointment abroad. She is young for her rank and friendly by disposition and possessing a cheerful independence of spirit. a Scot by birth and location.

We are giving a mammoth Closing Down Party. Everyone is coming. Admirals and their wives. A Bishop (I think), Hon Chaplains to various denominations. Other religious ranks (if indeed they do have ranks), everyone from HQ etc. It was going to be a GREAT PARTY.

The day came.

Our new Chief Officer concocted and mixed the Punch. When I saw what was going into it, I *trembled!* Then followed lemons and grapes. Then back to the bottles, without (as far as I could see) one glance at their labels!

It must be an old Scots recipe. The air about us was becoming aromatic… Should I hope or pray? Better do both.

Came the night, our Officers' Stewards looked marvellous, their coats whiter than white. Their hair-dos impeccable. We felt proud of them. Someone needed sandwiches for a late night duty. I must tell the Stewards.

The Director WRNS herself, drew me aside and said 'Tyler, I am appointing you to Plymouth when this establishment closes. I want you for Plymouth.'

PLYMOUTH!!

I had the most ghastly memories of Plymouth. James, do you recall my return from that extraordinary leave and finding my new Quarters spirited away in my absence? Of course, as it turned out, it was the best thing that could have happened, for in no time at all, Dartmouth cropped up. Still, I do believe that era has put me off Plymouth for life.

And in truth, I have given the matter considerable thought and had already decided that I was coming out of the Service once Mill Hill was handed over.

This I explained to the Director, who expressed regret. With a kind little speech of appreciation etc, she turned to the pursuit of the evening's social round. I had warned all the members of our Mess about the Punch. We had no casualties.

Well James, I have finally clinched it now. I am coming out of the Navy. I lie awake most nights trying to formulate plans but get not much further than tomorrow, for every 'tomorrow' must be planned in detail if we are handing over to the Medical Research Council on 2nd April.

This is my address until that final date, so please write.

Anna

In a train between
Kings Cross
and Yorkshire
2nd April 1946

Dear James

Yes, I have actually come this far. Into the train and homeward bound for Yorkshire. And with mixed feelings (the uppermost, just at this moment, being weariness).

We completed the closing down of Mill Hill and the handing over to the British Medical Council, without a hitch (Navy fashion)! But not without the most detailed planning, I assure you. One of our prior problems was the disposal of our non-Service property - 'Comforts' (for want of a better word), purchased at various times for the benefit and welfare of all personnel.

Payment for these comforts was allocated from any surplus monies left over from our messing allowance. Since they were valued in the yearly Official Audit, we were able to produce simple catalogues giving current value of each item, from the two pianos to chairs, cushions and flower vases.

To me the fairest way of disposing of these goods was to organise a raffle. No limit as to the number of tickets per person. Any Wren with a strong desire for a particular item could have friends buying tickets for her.

The proceeds of all this were donated to the WRNS Benevolent Fund. I cannot remember the final total but it exceeded everyone's expectations.

Our Chief Officer took a central position and drew the tickets. To my surprise, I got a piano! Not the Bechstein from our Wardroom but a good German upright. Since my sister has taken hers from home this is a piece of luck, indeed. In addition, I drew a small antique chair with buttoned back and a piano stool. I found a carrier service to Northallerton and made the arrangements for collection and delivery to Yorkshire and my home.

Wren numbers dwindled quickly as trainees were moved to an establishment in Berkshire.

Meanwhile I managed to find time to arrange to spend my six weeks' Release Leave in London and found an attractive Square, central but amazingly quiet, where there is a club for Women Service Officers. I have booked in for the six weeks (initially) and signed up for a course at a dress design school, run by a Frenchwoman.

But first I have to get my few possessions up to Yorkshire, which is what I am about at this moment. By mid-afternoon yesterday, everyone had departed from Mill Hill Quarters. That is, except Chief Officer and me and one Steward. There were one thousand personnel last year and now we were three (not counting what is in the cellars)!

Chief Officer and I took a taxi between us and she disembarked at Victoria Station on the way to her Overseas appointment. I continued to Kings Cross and took this train to Yorkshire, but will be returning next week to spend my Release Leave at the School of Dress Design, in preparation for what the future may hold.

Really, I do look forward to this. Though thinking back on my initial interview, I was not aware of any special enthusiasm on the school Principal's side as I answered her questions. I felt that I should be making more of a mark had I been speaking French (that is if I had been able to speak in understandable French). Well, even if they throw me out at the end of six weeks, I can add it to my long list of experiences.

And James, who better than you to know how long that list. Thank you for listening/reading and all your sympathy and cheerful encouragement, which so many times kept my head above those tricky waters!

'Til we meet…

Anna

APPENDIX

Explanation of some terms for the benefit of non-naval readers.

SHIP ~ A Naval Establishment, whether at sea or a building. All Ships mentioned in this book are shore-based establishments.

QUARTERS OFFICERS DUTIES ~ The duty of the Quarters Officer was to see that the ratings were quartered in a healthy, happy home.

QUARTERDECK ~ The after end of the upper deck of a ship between the quarters. Shore establishments selected a certain place, usually near the entrance, to be the Quarterdeck. The white ensign was hoisted at sunrise and lowered at sunset. All Naval personnel were required to Salute the Quarterdeck whenever they passed by it as a mark of respect paid to the authority of the Royal Navy.

MASTER AT ARMS ~ A warrant officer rank, or the senior chief petty officer of a ship. Used to be responsible for instructing men in the use of small arms, but later became head of the ship's police. Often referred to as 'Master'.

MESS TRAPS ~ This term included items of cutlery or crockery required for canteen facilities.

WARDROOM ~ Officers' Mess. All junior officers join ships and establishments as full members of the Wardroom Mess.

TRICORNE ~ Black ironed velour felt hat worn by Wren Officers.

GANGWAY SHEETS ~ These were written up every morning as a list of all personnel who were in port that day. The list had to state whether the men required feeding (Victualled In) or had left the Port (Checked Out); whether they were over 18 and to be issued with the daily ration of rum (Grog), or TT (Teetotal), or UA (Under Age and therefore not entitled to the ration of rum).

CAPTAIN'S COMMENDATION ~ The Captain commends the serviceman/woman before the assembled Ship's Company for a particular action taken by the person concerned in the course of his/her duty.

OTC ~ Officer Training Course
OIC ~ Officer in Charge
MTB ~ Motor Torpedo Boat
PMO ~ Port Medical Officer

Plumpton Hall, near Ripon, North Yorkshire ~ the family home

Launching Viking and Devon Maid off the embankment, Dartmouth.

Boatscrew Wrens at Sandquay, Dartmouth.

Wrens on the Balcony of the Rest Room on the Embankment at Dartmouth

Boatscrew Wrens take a break

Wrens march past the Dock to take part in VE Day Celebrations, May 1945

Looking between the Barrels of a Naval Gun, Wrens can be seen drilling on the Quarterdeck.

A Leading Wren Torpedoman working on a torpedo engine.

A Wren Radio Mechanic testing for defects in the W/T workshop

Dartmouth: Wrens sit happily in a boat on the river

(centre)

The author, and her two
assistants, the Quarters
Staff, at Skelmorlie, Largs,
Scotland ~ Summer 1945.

*Fleet Mail Wrens
perform their morning
delivery rounds to ships
in the anchorage.*

Naval servicemen collect their ration of rum from the victualling shed

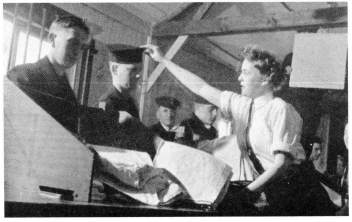

A Wren Supply Assistant kitting-up the young recruits

A *Boats' Crew come alongside to land their passengers and cargo.*

Firemen fighting back the flames of the towering furnace - Ave Maria Lane, 29th December 1940.

*Tube Stations became a valuable shelter for many a homeless Londoner -
November 1940*

Silhouetted against the light of the blaze, firemen climb into a building to help rescue people trapped on the upper floors.